D1328568

NOVEL DRILLING TECHNIQUES

NOVEL DRILLING TECHNIQUES

by

Dr. WILLIAM C. MAURER

Senior Research Specialist
Esso Production Research Company
Houston, Texas, U.S.A.

1968
THE QUEEN'S AWARD
TO INDUSTRY 1968

PERGAMON PRESS

OXFORD · LONDON · EDINBURGH · NEW YORK
TORONTO · SYDNEY · PARIS · BRAUNSCHWEIG

Pergamon Press Ltd., Headington Hill Hall, Oxford
4 & 5 Fitzroy Square, London W.1
Pergamon Press (Scotland) Ltd., 2 & 3 Teviot Place, Edinburgh 1
Pergamon Press Inc., 44–01 21st Street, Long Island City, New York 11101
Pergamon of Canada, Ltd., 6 Adelaide Street East, Toronto, Ontario
Pergamon Press (Aust.) Pty. Ltd., Rushcutters Bay, Sydney, N.S.W.
Pergamon Press S.A.R.L., 24 rue des Écoles, Paris 5ᵉ
Vieweg & Sohn GmbH, Burgplatz 1, Braunschweig

Copyright © 1968
William C. Maurer

First edition 1968

This monograph is issued under the auspices of the
International Journal of Rock Mechanics and Mining Sciences

Library of Congress Catalog Card No. 68-17738

PRINTED IN GREAT BRITAIN BY A. WHEATON & CO., EXETER

08 003615 5

TO MY WIFE, KATHY

Contents

Acknowledgments

THE author would like to acknowledge the cooperation and assistance of the following persons:

DR. J. J. BAILEY—Creare, Inc., Hanover, New Hampshire, U.S.A.

MR. J. J. DALY—Atlas Copco, Hackensack, New Jersey, U.S.A.

MR. J. DELACOUR—Institut Français du Pétrole, Rueil-Malmaison, France.

DR. I. W. FARMER—University College, Cardiff, England.

MESSRS. L. B. GELLER and W. M. GRAY—Dept. of Energy, Mines and Resources, Ottawa, Canada.

MR. S. J. LEACH—Safety in Mines Research Establishment, Sheffield, England.

MESSRS. N. G. MAROUDAS and E. A. NEPPIRAS—Imperial College of Science and Technology, London, England.

MR. R. L. MAROVELLI—Bureau of Mines Research Center, Minneapolis, Minnesota, U.S.A.

MR. JEAN RAYNAL—Société Nationale des Pétroles d'Aquitaine, Pau, France.

DR. JOHN S. RINEHART—Environmental Science Services Administration, Boulder, Colorado, U.S.A.

PROF. A. ROBERTS—University of Sheffield, Sheffield, England.

DR. ERICH SARAPUU—Electrofrac Corporation, Kansas City, Missouri, U.S.A.

The author would also like to express his appreciation to Esso Production Research Company for assistance in preparing the manuscript. Special appreciation is expressed to Mr. R. T. Schweisberger, who translated numerous Russian articles on novel drilling techniques.

CHAPTER 1

Introduction

CONSIDERABLE research is going on throughout the world to develop new methods for drilling and excavating rock. In this study novel drills are defined as those which do not use conventional bits to attack rock. Considerable research is being done to develop bottom-hole drilling motors such as electric drills and turbodrills. These motors, which use conventional bits, are described in detail by Ledgerwood and will not be considered in this study. Although the devices described in this study are called novel, many of the concepts involved are quite old, as evidenced by the fact that the first flame drill was patented in 1853 and the first electric arc drill was patented in 1874. What we choose to call novel devices remove rock by four basic mechanisms: mechanically induced stresses, thermally induced stresses, fusion and vaporization, and chemical reactions. These devices have potential applications wherever rock is drilled, crushed, or excavated. They also have potential applications for drilling and machining materials such as metals, ceramics, and glass.

Many of these novel techniques have been shown in laboratory tests to drill or excavate rock effectively, but few of them have been tested on a large scale. One problem in developing these new drilling or excavating techniques is that they are competing with conventional tools that have undergone many years of improvement. For example, the penetration rates of oilfield rotary drills are 10–100 times faster than when these drills were first introduced in 1884. Similar improvements can be expected with novel methods once they are put into routine use. This is an important factor to consider when evaluating new techniques from preliminary laboratory or field tests.

Novel rock destruction methods will probably find initial application where rate of rock removal is more important than unit cost, such as in some military applications. They will also find application where restrictions are imposed on the rock destruction device (such as weight limitation in space exploration or size limitation in deep

1

oil wells). Once novel methods find initial application, they will be refined and improved until their costs are reduced to the point where they find more widespread application in industry.

Improvements are continually being made on equipment and techniques, so these new devices must be continually re-evaluated. Because of these continued improvements, some of the new drilling and excavating methods not economical today may find application in a few years. An important thing to remember when evaluating these new devices is that what is exotic today may be conventional tomorrow.

CHAPTER 2

Basic Rock Destruction Mechanisms

MACHINES drill and excavate rock by four basic mechanisms: mechanically induced stresses, thermally induced stresses, fusion and vaporization, and chemical reactions. Fundamentals involved in each of these mechanisms are described below.

Mechanically Induced Stresses

Novel drills produce mechanically induced stresses by impact, abrasion, and erosion. When these stresses exceed a rock's tensile or shear strength, brittle fracturing or plastic yielding takes place.

Impact loads are produced by percussion tools, implosions, explosions, and underwater spark discharges. These impacts usually produce a zone of finely crushed rock directly beneath the area of impact. If sufficient force and energy are applied to the rock, fractures are initiated around this crushed zone. These fractures propagate along curved trajectories to the rock surface, breaking loose chips or fragments of rock (Maurer).

Abrasion devices use hard, particulate materials such as diamond or tungsten carbide to abrade and remove rock. The particles usually move nearly parallel to the rock surface, producing a crushed zone ahead of them and planing a groove into the rock. If the depth of cut is sufficient, fractures propagate along curved trajectories from the tip of the abrasive particle to the rock surface, forming chips ahead of the abrasive particle.

Erosion jets can be classed as low-speed, abrasive jets (10–200 m/sec) that use sand or other abrasive particles to impact and remove the rock, or high-speed erosion jets (200–1000 m/sec) that use water to erode the rock. The high-speed erosion jets, which require pressures up to 5000 kg/cm², can drill holes in the hardest rocks. High-pressure jets have an action similar to that of a series of solid projectiles striking the rock surfaces (Farmer and Attewell). Leach and

For a typical quartz crystal ($a = 8 \times 10^{-6}$ °C^{-1}; $E = 9 \times 10^5$ kg/cm^2) constrained in one direction and heated to 100°C this induced stress will equal 720 kg/cm^2.

Induced stresses are higher when thermal strains are constrained in more than one direction, e.g. parallel to a heated surface. The example above shows that although the thermal strains are not completely constrained around a crystal in a rock, thermal stresses of sufficient magnitude to break any rock can be created by relatively small increases in temperature.

When the surfaces of many rocks are rapidly heated, thin layers flake off the surface. This phenomenon, which is usually called thermal spalling, produces very thin flakes, or spalls, as shown in Fig. 1.

Size and shape of these spalls is controlled by the temperature gradient into the rock. Devices such as the jet-piercing drill heat the rock over a relatively large area, in which case the temperature gradient into the rock can be closely approximated by the temperature distribution for constant heat flux into a semi-infinite surface (Carslaw and Jaeger):

$$T(x, t) = 2F \sqrt{(Kt)}/k \ i \ erfc \ [x/2 \ \sqrt{(Kt)}], \qquad (2)$$

where T = temperature rise above initial temperature, °C;
F = constant heat flux into surface, cal/cm^2 sec;
k = thermal conductivity, cal/cm sec °C;
c = specific heat, cal/g °C;
ρ = density, g/cm^3;
$K = k/\rho c$ = diffusivity, cm^2/sec;
x = depth below rock surface, cm;
t = time, sec.

The temperature at the rock surface ($x = 0$) equals

$$T_0 = \frac{2F}{k} \sqrt{(Kt/\pi)}. \qquad (3)$$

These equations show that diffusivity has an important bearing on the heat flow and temperature gradient into the rock. Calaman and Rolseth found that rocks with high diffusivity are usually most susceptible to spalling.

The exact heat flux into the rock surface during jet-piercing drilling is not known because of the complicated mechanisms involved. Just

(1963) calculated a heat flux of 200 cal/cm² sec into the rock surface, based on flame diameter, flame temperature, mass rate of heat flow, and specific heat. Gray assumed a heat flux of 253 cal/cm² sec and used the following values for granite, $\rho = 2.6$ g/cm³, $k = 0.006$ cal/cm sec °C, and $c = 0.2$ cal/g °C to calculate that the surface of granite is heated from 0° to 500°C in 0.01 sec and from 0° to 1000°C in 0.04 sec, producing the temperature gradient shown in Fig. 2. The temperature decreases from 1000°C at the rock surface to 0°C at a depth of 0.8 mm, which explains why these spalls are very thin. Gray assumed that when spalls form, the surface of the rock is at 1000°C

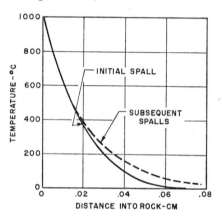

Fig. 2. Temperature gradient into rock during thermal spalling (Gray).

and the bottom of the spall at 500°C, which would result in a spall 0.15 mm thick. Following formation of the spall, the newly created surface would be heated from 500° to 1000°C in 0.03 sec, forming another spall. This process repeats itself. For steady-state spalling, the thermal gradient at the instant these successive spalls are formed is shown by the dashed line in Fig. 2. Under these conditions, the spalling rate would equal 18 m/hr (0.15 mm/0.03 sec), which closely corresponds to drilling rates in highly spallable rock and indicates that this spalling model is realistic.

Browning *et al.* describe tests in which thermocouples were imbedded in granite in the path of approaching jet-piercing flames. With high-power densities, the surface of the granite was heated to a spalling temperature of around 500°C; the temperature decreased to the initial rock temperature at a depth of only 1.6 mm below the surface. As the power density was decreased, the length of the temperature gradient increased until finally only fusion occurred at the rock surface due to the absence of steep thermal gradients. In this case, the heat penetrated a great distance into the rock. These experimental results support the theoretical results obtained by Gray.

Instead of spalling, many rocks degrade and lose strength when heated. In some rocks, this thermal degradation continues to a point at which the rocks can be easily crumbled or broken. Rocks often undergo thermal degradation when they are uniformly heated, e.g. between capacitor plates or in a magnetic coil, because steep temperature gradients are not present to cause thermal spalling. Thermal degradation is usually accompanied by cracking sounds as thermal expansion breaks bonds between grains and crystals. Degradation can also result from chemical changes such as the decomposition of calcium carbonate in limestone and marble.

Since thermal degradation usually does not break rock completely, some mechanical means is required to crush or drill the weakened rock. This suggests the possibility of combining some of the novel devices with each other or with conventional methods. For example, a plasma or laser could be used to heat and degrade rock while high-voltage sparks or high-speed erosion jets could be used to crush and remove the weakened rock. This could be especially advantageous in hard rock such as granite, for which drilling is slow and dulling of the cutting tools is a problem.

Fusion and Vaporization

The total energy H required to fuse and vaporize rock equals

$$H = c_s\,(T_m - T_i) + H_f + c_m\,(T_v - T_m) + H_v \quad \text{[cal/g]}, \qquad (4)$$

where
c_s = mean specific heat of solid rock, cal/g °C;
c_m = mean specific heat of molten rock, cal/g °C;
T_i = initial temperature of rock, °C;
T_m = melting temperature of rock, °C;
T_v = vaporization temperature of rock, °C;
H_f = latent heat of fusion, cal/g;
H_v = latent heat of vaporization, cal/g.

Table 1 shows that about 4000 to 5000 joules/cm³ is required to fuse most rocks. It is interesting that less energy is required to fuse strong, igneous rocks such as granite and basalt than to fuse sedimentary rocks such as sandstone and limestone. This suggests that

Novel Drilling Techniques

TABLE 1. *Heat Required to Fuse Various Materials.*

Material	Specific gravity (g/cm³)	Specific heat (cal/g°C)	Melting point (°C)	Latent heat of fusion (cal/g)	Total heat of fusion	
					(cal/g)	(joules/cm³)
Ice	0.92	0.47	0	80	80	310
Aluminum	2.7	0.25	660	77	240	2720
Glass	2.6	0.19	1100	50	260	2850
Granite	2.7	0.24	1250	80	380	4320
Basalt	2.8	0.24	1150	100	375	4400
Sandstone	2.2	0.24	1650	80	480	4440
Quartz	2.7	0.26	1610	30	450	5110
Steel	7.8	0.11	1500	80	245	8000
Limestone[a]	2.6	0.24	2600	120	980	10700

[a] $CaCO_3$ decomposes to CaO at 895°C, requiring 425 cal/g.

fusion drills will find initial application for drilling strong rocks where bit-dulling is a problem.

Considerably more energy is required to vaporize materials than is required to fuse them. For example, only 80 cal/g is required to melt ice, whereas an additional 640 cal/g is required to vaporize the water. Limited available data indicate that the energy required to vaporize rock is very high. For example, only 450 cal/g is required to fuse quartz, while over 2000 cal/g is required to vaporize silica (Ostrovskii). This indicates that for constant power output, drills which fuse rocks will drill much faster than those which vaporize rock.

Chemical Reactions

A wide variety of chemicals can be used to dissolve different types of rock. Chemical drills use highly reactive chemicals (such as fluorine or one of the other halogens) to produce high-speed reactions with rock. These violent reactions, which are of sufficient intensity to set fire to asbestos, produce harmless products that can be easily removed. Laboratory tests have shown that these chemicals can effectively drill sandstone, limestone, and granite (Refs. 69 and 95).

CHAPTER 3

Crushing and Drilling-rate Equations

IN ORDER to break rock by mechanically or thermally induced stresses, sufficient force or energy must be applied to the rock that the induced stresses will exceed the rock's strength. Similarly, when fusing rock sufficient heat must be applied to produce local temperatures that exceed the melting temperature of the rock. Once these threshold values of force or energy are exceeded, the amount of energy required to break or remove a unit volume of rock remains nearly constant (Teale). This energy parameter, which is a measure of the efficiency of the rock destruction technique, is defined as *specific energy* in this study. Since this energy parameter is nearly constant, it is useful for predicting the performance of large-scale drills or rock crushers from laboratory tests.

Crushing Equations

The rate at which rock can be crushed, C.R., equals

$$\text{C.R.} = P/E \quad [\text{cm}^3/\text{min}], \qquad (5)$$

where P = power input to the rock, joules/min;
E = specific energy, joules/cm^3.

Bond has obtained considerable rock-crushing data that show the specific energy can be closely approximated by the relationship

$$E = 10E_i \left(\frac{1}{\sqrt{p}} - \frac{1}{\sqrt{f}} \right) \quad [\text{joules/cm}^3], \qquad (6)$$

where E_i = specific energy required to crush rock from infinite size to 100 microns, joules/cm^3;
f = initial particle size, microns;
p = final particle size, microns.

9

When a considerable size reduction occurs ($f \gg p$), eq. (6) reduces to

$$E \approx \frac{10\,E_i}{\sqrt{p}}, \tag{7}$$

in which case the specific energy is inversely proportional to the square root of the particle size. Table 2 gives typical values of specific energy for crushing various rocks.

TABLE 2. *Typical Specific Energy Requirements for Conventional Crushing (joules/cm³).*[a]

Rock	Crushed particle size		
	0.1 mm	1 mm	10 mm
Glass	30	10	3
Sandstone	110	35	11
Limestone	110	35	11
Dolomite	110	35	11
Quartzite	120	38	12
Quartz	120	38	12
Granite	140	45	14
Shale	150	48	15
Taconite	180	57	18
Basalt	210	67	21

[a] Ref.: Bond.

Drilling-rate Equations

Drilling rate, R, can be expressed as

$$R = P/AE \quad \text{[cm/min]}, \tag{8}$$

where P = power transmitted to the rock, joules/min;
A = hole cross-section area, cm²;
E = specific energy, joules/cm³.

When only part of the power output of the drill is transmitted to the rock, the drilling-rate equation can be expressed as

$$R = eP_o/AE \quad \text{[cm/min]}, \tag{9}$$

where P_o = power output of the drill, joules/min;
e = drill-to-rock power transmission efficiency.

Equations (8) and (9) are useful for estimating drilling rate from laboratory tests and for relating drilling rate in holes of different diameter or for drills with different power outputs.

CHAPTER 4

Performance Characteristics of Conventional Drills

IN ORDER to evaluate new drilling methods, it is necessary to know the operating characteristics of conventional drills. Table 3 gives the power outputs and typical drilling rates for rotary and percussive drills in soft, medium, and hard rock (where medium-strength rocks are arbitrarily defined as having uniaxial compressive strengths of 500–1000 kg/cm²). Drilling rates may differ from the values of Table 3, because other rock properties such as plasticity and porosity affect drilling rate. Nevertheless, these typical drilling rates give a good basis for comparison between conventional and novel drilling methods.

Table 3 shows that the specific energy required to drill most rocks at atmosphere pressure with conventional drills ranges from about 50 to 1000 joules/cm³. Diamond drills require higher energy, because they crush the rock into much smaller fragments. The cutting mechanisms of conventional drills are very efficient and require less energy than nearly all of the novel drills considered in this study. Although the novel drills require more energy, several of them can drill faster than conventional drills because they can transmit more power to the rock. For example, a jet-piercing drill has a power output of 500–1000 h.p., while the largest oilfield rotary rigs can transmit only 20–40 h.p. to the rock. This low power transmission to the rock is the main limitation of conventional drills.

There is considerable incentive for improving drilling techniques in deep oil and gas wells because of high costs and low drilling rates. New drilling methods may therefore find initial application in these deep wells. The incremental drilling cost below 15,000 ft often ranges from $50 to more than $100 a foot, since these large rigs cost $1000–$3000 a day for land drilling and $5000–$30,000 a day for offshore drilling. Replacing dull bits in these deep wells is costly, because 10–15 hr may often be required to pull the drill pipe from the hole to

TABLE 3. *Typical Drilling Rates for Conventional Drills at Atmospheric Pressure.*

Drill	Average hole size (cm)	Power transmitted to rock (h.p.)	Typical drilling rate (cm/min) Rock type[a]				Specific energy (joules/cm³) Rock type[a]			
			Soft	Medium	Hard	Very hard	Soft	Medium	Hard	Very hard
Percussive										
Jackhammer	3.8	5	Used only		75	50	—	—	260	390
Drifter	4.8	9	for		120	80	—	—	180	270
Blasthole	7.6	11	hard rocks		60	40	—	—	180	270
Rotary (mining)										
Roller	20	30	200	100	20	5	20	40	210	840
Drag	10	15	400	200	100	Dulls	20	40	80	—
Diamond	5	10	Not used		20	5	—	—	1120	4500
Rotary (oil field)										
Roller drag	20	30	50	10	5	2	80	420	840	2100
Drag	20	50	100	20	Not used		70	350	—	—
Diamond	20	20	20	5	2	1	140	560	1400	2800
Jet-piercing	20	160[b]	Not used			15	—	—	—	1500

Rock type	Compressive strength (kg/cm²)
Soft	0–500
Medium	500–1000
Hard	1000–2000
Very hard	>2000

[b] Power output is 500–1000 h.p., but only 100–200 h.p. is transmitted to the rock.

TABLE 4. *Effect of Well Depth on Oilfield Rotary Drilling Rate.*

Well depth (m)	Typical drilling rates (m/hr)			Typical specific energy (joules/cm^3)		
	Rock type[a]			Rock type[a]		
	Soft	Mediu	Hard	Soft	Medium	Hard
0–2000	15–50	5–15	1–5	50– 170	170– 510	510–2600
2000–4000	10–30	4–10	1–4	85– 260	260– 640	640–2600
4000–6000	6–20	2–6	1–2	130– 430	430–1300	1300–2600
6000–8000	1–2	1–2	1–2	1300–2600	1300–2600	1300–2600

[a] Soft rock   Comp. str. <500 kg/cm^2.
Medium rock Comp. str. = 500–1000 kg/cm^2.
Hard rock   Comp. str. >1000 kg/cm^2.

change bits. (Conventional roller and drag bits dull after 10–20 hr rotating time, while diamond bits dull after 50–200 hr, so these bits have to be replaced often.) These high costs furnish considerable incentive for increasing drilling rate and for developing a drill that can work at the hole bottom for longer periods of time. Considerable savings could also be realized by using a drilling method which would require a lighter drilling rig or fewer crew members.

Drilling rate decreases rapidly with increasing well depth because of the increased pressure exerted against the hole bottom by the column of drilling fluid in the well. High fluid pressure reduces drilling rate by increasing the rock strength and by creating chip-removal problems beneath the bit (Maurer, 1962). In deep wells, considerable energy is wasted in regrinding cuttings separated from the rock but not flushed from beneath the bit. Table 4 gives typical oilfield drilling rates as a function of hole depth for different rocks. At shallow depths, bottom-hole cleaning is relatively good and weak rocks drill 10–50 times faster than hard rocks. As the well depth increases, rock-cuttings removal becomes a problem and some of the weaker rocks begin to yield in a plastic-like manner (Maurer, 1965). As a result, the difference in drilling rates between weak and hard rocks decreases with increasing hole depth until in very deep wells they often drill at similar rates. In some deep wells, hard rocks may fail in a brittle manner and drill faster than weaker rocks that fail in a plastic manner and create bottom-hole cleaning problems.

CHAPTER 5

Methods of Drilling and Breaking Rock by Mechanically Induced Stresses

Turbine Drills

Humble Oil & Refining Company (Cannon) and Christensen Diamond Products Company (Ref. 103) have done considerable development work on the turbine drill shown in Fig. 3. This drill uses a single-stage turbine to rotate a diamond-faced cutter wheel at 5000–10,000 rev/min at the bottom of a drill pipe. The drill pipe is rotated at 30–75 rev/min to produce a hemispherical bottom-hole contour. Part of the load applied to the turbine drill is transmitted to the rock through diamond reamers at the bottom of the drill, and part of it is applied to the spring-loaded cutter wheel. Sufficient load is applied to the drill to ensure that the reamers contact the rock. Operating characteristics of a field model turbine drill are given in Table 5.

TABLE 5. *Turbine Drill Operating Characteristics.*[a]

Turbine speed	5000–10,000 rev/min
Drill pipe speed	30–75 rev/min
Hole diameter	20 cm
Total load on turbine drill	1500–2500 kg
Spring load on turbine wheel	500–1500 kg
Hydraulic power	200–300 h.p.
Turbine power	$\approx$ 20–60 h.p.
Turbine efficiency	$\approx$ 10–20 percent

[a] Ref.: Cannon.

The power output P of the turbine drill equals

$$P = 2\pi NT \quad [\text{kg-m/min}], \tag{10}$$

where N = turbine rotary speed, rev/min;
T = torque on the cutter wheel, kg-m.

15

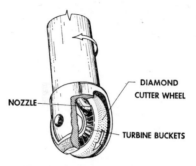

NOZZLE

DIAMOND
CUTTER WHEEL

TURBINE BUCKETS

FIG. 3. Turbine drill (Cannon).

Turbine speed decreases as the torque increases; the cutter wheel "runs away" at low torques and stalls at high torques. Maximum power output occurs between 5000 and 10,000 rev/min. Since the turbine's power output is controlled by the cutter-wheel torque, it is important to optimize the thrust on the spring-loaded cutter wheel. Christensen Diamond Products Company established a series of torque curves for turbine drills in different rocks; the curves permit optimization of the spring load in the field. Some power is transmitted to the rock through the reamers, but this is usually small compared to the turbine's power output (because of the low rotary speed of the drill pipe).

Several turbine drills were tested in oilfield drilling from 1953 to 1956. Initially, failure of the cutting elements and fluid erosion of the turbine buckets were problems, but these difficulties were overcome. Results of field tests comparing rotary and turbine drills are given in Table 6. The rotary drills penetrated about twice as fast as the turbine drills, except in Well 4 where the rotary bit load had to be reduced 50 percent because of hole deviation. In this case, the turbine drilled 15 percent faster than the rotary drill.

The exact turbine power output in these tests was unknown, but it was on the order of 20 h.p. Based on this power output, the specific energy ranged from 360 to 1300 joules/cm^3, which is slightly higher than that for conventional diamond bits (Table 3). This is expected, because the bottom-hole cleaning conditions with the turbine drill are not as good due to the high rotary speed, which causes regrinding of cuttings and wasted power.

Application of the turbine drill appears to be limited; the single-stage turbine is only 10–20 percent efficient and has a power output

TABLE 6. *Turbine Drilling Data.*[a]

Well number	Drill	Hole dia. (cm)	Drilling distance (m)	Drilling time (hr)	Drilling rate (m/hr)	Specific[b] energy (joules/cm^3)
1	Turbine	20	33	7.3	4.6	360
	Rotary	20	67	10.9	6.1	—
2	Turbine	20	16	12.1	1.3	1300
	Rotary	20	18	6.1	3.0	—
3	Turbine	20	21	9.9	2.2	750
	Rotary	20	67	10.7	6.3	—
4	Turbine	20	16	10.9	1.5	1100
	Rotary[c]	20	10	7.9	1.3	—

[a] Ref.: Cannon.
[b] Exact turbine power output unknown, specific energy based on 20 h.p. output.
[c] Bit load reduced 50 percent by a hole deviation problem.

of only 20–60 h.p. This power output is comparable to that of rotary drills. Since diamond bits require about twice as much specific energy as roller bits (Table 3), turbine drills are limited to drilling rates about half those of rotary drills. Significant improvements in the efficiency and power output of the turbine drill will require the use of either a different type of single-stage turbine or a multistage turbine. Work is currently inactive on this drill and no commercial models are available.

Pellet Drills

Carter Oil Company (Eckel *et al.*) made a detailed study of a pellet drill (Fig. 4) that uses steel pellets to impact and break rock. These

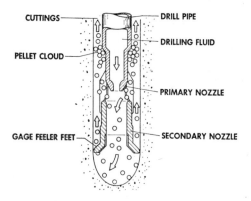

FIG. 4. Pellet drill (Eckel *et al.*).

pellets remain at the hole bottom and are recirculated through the bit. The concept with this drill was to develop a well-drilling tool with cutting elements that could be replaced without pulling the drill pipe from the hole. Table 7 gives the operating characteristics of a 23 cm diameter laboratory pellet drill. This drill circulates 3.2 cm diameter steel pellets at the rate of 140 pellets/sec.

Drilling fluid is pumped down the drill pipe and through a primary nozzle, producing an aspirator action that forces the pellets into the drill. The pellets accelerate to a velocity of 23 m/sec in the secondary nozzle and then strike against the rock. The pellets and broken rock are lifted by the rising fluid to the secondary nozzles aspirator openings, through which four-fifths of the fluid is recirculated through the

TABLE 7. *Pellet Drill Operating Characteristics.*[a]

Bit diameter	23 cm
Rotary speed	20 rev/min
Flow rate	1970 l./min
Primary nozzle pressure drop	40.5 kg/cm^2
Primary nozzle diameter	2.2 cm
Secondary nozzle diameter	8.9 cm
Pellet diameter	3.2 cm
Pellet charge	65–85 kg
Impact rate	140 pellets/sec
Impact velocity	23 m/sec
Hydraulic power	172 h.p.
Pellet power	6.4 h.p.
Hydraulic efficiency	3.7 percent

[a] Ref.: Eckel *et al.*

drill; the remaining fluid carries the cuttings up through the annulus to the surface. The steel pellets remain suspended in a "cloud" (due to the reduced fluid velocity) until they randomly drop from the cloud and recirculate through the bit. Two "gage feeler" feet at the bottom of the drill maintain proper stand-off distance between the bit and the rock. The pellet drill must be rotated slowly to expose the formation beneath these feet.

Table 8 shows that pellet drilling rates ranged from 0.25 cm/min in hard pink quartzite to 3.8 cm/min in soft Oklahoma marble. Pellet wear was extremely low and was noticeable only in pink quartzite, in which 64 kg of pellets lost 1.1 kg of steel during a 3.5 hr test. Based on the pellet output power, specific energy in these drilling tests ranged from 130 to 2500 joules/cm^3, which is comparable to the energy required by conventional drills. Based on the hydraulic input power specific energy ranged from 3500 to 67,000 joules/cm^3, which is much higher than for conventional drills.

The main limitation of the pellet drill is that only about 4 percent of the hydraulic power is transmitted to the pellets. Eckel *et al.* made a detailed study of 26 variables affecting the hydraulic efficiency and found that the most important variables are the diameters of the primary and secondary nozzles, the size of the pellets, the length of the secondary nozzle, the stand-off distance, the flow rate, and the type of fluid. They found that water was the best drilling fluid; drilling mud (1.15 g/cm^3) reduced the drilling rate by 25 percent, and

TABLE 8. *Pellet Drilling Data.*[a]

Rock	Hole dia. (cm)	Drilling rate (cm/min)	Hydraulic power (h.p.)	Pellet power (h.p.)	Specific energy (joules/cm³)	
					Input[b]	Output[c]
Oklahoma marble (weak)	27	3.8	172	6.4	3,500	130
Virginia limestone (medium)	25	2.0	172	6.4	7,700	290
Pink quartzite (strong)	24	0.25	172	6.4	67,000	2,500

[a] Ref.: Eckel *et al.*
[b] Based on hydraulic power to drill.
[c] Based on pellet power to rock.

air reduced the drilling rate by 75 percent. Results of this study were used to optimize these variables in the 23 cm pellet drill, resulting in a maximum efficiency of only 3.7 percent.

Many pellet drills other than the one shown in Fig. 4 were tested. One drill used a sharp cutting edge to mechanically cut the gage of the hole while the pellets removed the center of the hole (Eckel, 1967). This drill, which required a thrust of 200–400 kg, drilled sandstone and limestone at instantaneous drilling rates in excess of 30 m/hr. Despite this high drilling rate, this drill was not practical because it failed rapidly due to pellet erosion of the mechanical cutting edge.

Because of the detailed nature of this investigation (in which over 35 pellet drilling devices were tested), it appears that major improvements can be made on the pellet drill only by making major changes in the basic concepts of this drill. Pellet drill development is currently inactive, and no commercial tools are available.

Continuous Penetrators

Howe has proposed the continuous penetrator shown in Fig. 5 for drilling porous rock or unconsolidated material. The penetrator would crush the rock and displace it into a zone of crushed rock surrounding the hole. This penetrator would obviate pulling drill pipe to the surface to replace worn bits, and it would require no circulating fluid to remove the cuttings. The high forces required for penetration would be produced by the weight of drill collars, by impact loads, or by wall anchors which grip the borehole walls and hydraulically load the penetrator. Wall anchors of this type have been successfully tested in oilwells (Kellner and Roberts).

The penetrator would produce a zone of crushed rock surrounding the hole; this zone would have a radius r equal to

$$r = r_o \bigg/ \sqrt{\left(\frac{1 - \phi_c}{\phi - \phi_c}\right)},$$ (11)

where r_o = radius of penetrator;
ϕ = porosity of solid rock;
ϕ_c = porosity of crushed rock.

In general, the porosity of the solid rock would be much greater than that of the crushed zone ($\phi \gg \phi_c$) and ϕ_c would be much less than unity, in which case eq. (11) reduces to

$$r \approx r_o / \sqrt{\phi}.$$ (12)

This crushed zone can be very large in rocks with low porosity. For example, the radius of a crushed zone in a rock with 5 percent porosity would be more than 4 times the radius of the penetrator.

The author has observed similar crushed zones surrounding holes produced by projectiles penetrating porous rocks. In these tests, the average deceleration force on 0.7 cm diameter projectiles penetrating porous sandstone was 3000 kg. Static tests and impact tests in unconsolidated material indicated that most of this force was used to overcome the strength of the rock; only a small part was due to inertia of the crushed rock ahead of the projectile. By similitude, the force on a penetrator should be proportional to the projected cross-sectional area, which indicates that forces on the order of 1–5 million

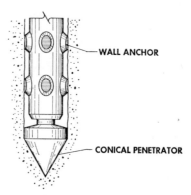

FIG. 5. Continuous penetrator (Howe).

kg would be required on a 20 cm diameter penetrator in porous sandstone. These high forces appear to make the continuous penetrator impractical for drilling medium- or high-strength rocks.

Since the penetrator produces a zone of crushed rock, it should be possible to use a smaller penetrator and to mechanically or hydraulically ream out the crushed zone surrounding the hole. In this case, a circulating fluid would be required to remove the crushed rock from the hole. Equation (12) shows that a 5 cm diameter penetrator would produce a crushed zone large enough to be reamed out to a 20 cm diameter hole in a hole with 5 percent porosity. This would reduce the average force required on the penetrator in porous sandstone from about 3 million kg to about 180,000 kg. In very weak rocks with high porosities, these forces would be considerably lower. Because of the high forces required, the continuous penetrator appears to have potential application only in weak, highly porous rocks or in unconsolidated material.

Implosion Drills

Ostrovskii has proposed an implosion drill for drilling oil wells. This drill would produce implosions by pumping hermetically sealed capsules to the hole bottom and breaking them against the rock by impact or by other means, as shown in Fig. 6. The high hydrostatic

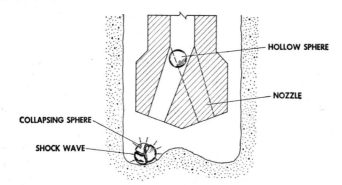

FIG. 6. Implosion drill (Ostrovskii).

pressure in the well would produce intense implosions in the collapsing cavities, thus creating high-pressure pulses which would impact and break the rock.

Rayleigh has shown that the pressure P during the collapse of a spherical vacuum bubble in an idealized incompressible liquid equals

$$P = 0.163\,(R_o/R)^3 P_o \quad [\text{kg/cm}^2],\qquad(13)$$

where R_o = initial radius of the cavity, cm;
R = instantaneous radius, cm;
P_o = hydrostatic pressure, kg/cm².

Pressures in these collapsing cavities can be very large. For example, a collapse pressure of 32,600 kg/cm² is produced when a 50 mm radius cavity collapses to a 5 mm radius in a 2000 m deep oil well filled with water ($P_o = 200$ kg/cm²). The hydraulic impact pressure on the rock will be somewhat lower, because the collapse pressure is produced a few centimeters from the rock and because the fluid is not incompressible, as is assumed in eq. (13).

The energy E released by an implosion equals the product of the hydrostatic pressure and the cavity volume:

$$E = 4/3 \ \pi R_o^3 P_o \quad \text{[kg-cm]}. \tag{14}$$

Equation (14) shows that a 10 cm diameter cavity would yield about 1000 kg-m (9800 joules) energy at a depth of 2000 m ($P_o = 200$ kg/cm^2). This is equivalent to the energy released by about 2 g of TNT.

The power output P of an implosion drill is

$$P = 9.31 \times 10^{-7} \ nwhR_o^3 \quad \text{[h.p.]}, \tag{15}$$

where

$n =$ capsule pumping rate, capsules/min;
$w =$ density of fluid in wellbore, g/cm^3;
$h =$ well depth, m;
$R_o =$ initial radius of capsule cavity, cm.

This shows that power output of an implosion drill increases with capsule size, pumping rate, fluid density, and well depth. This indicates that implosion drills would be most effective in deep oilwells where the fluid pressure is high.

The implosion rock-failure mechanism will probably require more energy than do rotary drills, since part of the energy is dissipated in the fluid. Consequently, implosion drills will require power outputs higher than the 20–50 h.p. which large rotary drills transmit to the rock. Equation (15) shows that a 50 h.p. implosion drill would require 13,000 10 cm diameter spheres per hour at a drilling depth of 2000 m. Most likely, implosion capsules would be expensive to make and the quantities needed would be difficult to handle; these factors indicate implosion drilling would be impractical.

The author made a series of tests using capsules containing 1 cm diameter × 10 cm long cavities to produce implosions on Indiana limestone and Berea sandstone at hydrostatic pressures up to 800 kg/cm^2. In all these tests the capsules were shattered into fine particles by the implosions but the rocks were unaffected, indicating that implosions are an ineffective method of breaking rock.

Spark Drills

High-voltage underwater spark discharges produce explosive-like pressure pulses capable of drilling and breaking rock. The operating characteristics of a laboratory spark or "electrohydraulic" drill used by Titkov *et al.* are given in Table 9. Under the influence of a powerful electrical field, a thin, conducting channel of ionized gas forms between the electrodes. Energy stored in the condensers flows through this small conducting zone, creating a high-temperature plasma that exerts a pressure on the order of 10^4–10^5 atm on the water confining the spark (Martin). These sparks last from 5 to 50 μsec, producing

TABLE 9. *Spark Drill Operating Characteristics.*[a]

Hole diameter	3 cm
Spark rate	120–330 sparks/min
Spark duration	1–10 μsec
Spark pressure	10,000–20,000 kg/cm^2
Capacitance	0.1–0.3 μf
Charging potential	30–50 kV
Spark energy	45–375 joules
Rock removal rate	0.1–1 cm^3/spark
Rocks drilled	Marble, shale, granite

[a] Ref.: Yutkin.

instantaneous power outputs in excess of 1 million h.p. These underwater sparks are used commercially as seismic sources and for forming metals. When fired in air, these high-energy sparks are not effective for breaking rock, because air is highly compressible and allows the spark to expand without creating high pressures.

The energy E released during a spark discharge is

$$E = 1/2\ CV^2 \quad \text{[joules]}, \tag{15}$$

where C is the capacitance (microfarads) and V is the charging potential (kilovolts). The power output P of a spark drill or spark crusher equals

$$P = 0.00067\ nCV^2 \quad \text{[h.p.]}, \tag{16}$$

where n is the spark discharge rate (sparks per second).

Energy released by a 4 μf condenser charged to 70 kv equals 9800 joules, which is equivalent to the energy released by about 2 g of TNT. A spark drill firing 10 of these sparks per second would have a power output of 133 h.p., which is considerably higher than the 20–50 h.p. that large rotary rigs can transmit to rock.

Titkov *et al.* used the tangential spark drill shown in Fig. 7 to drill various rocks. This drill discharges sparks between electrodes around the periphery of the drill. In these tests, a 0.26 μf condenser charged to 50 kv was discharged 330 times a minute, producing a power output of 2.4 h.p. A 2.1 cm diameter hole was drilled in dolomite (compressive strength = 225 kg/cm²) at the rate of 0.67 cm/min, corresponding to a specific energy of 465 joules/cm³.

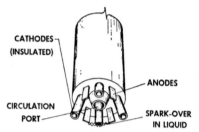

FIG. 7. Tangential spark drill (Titkov *et al.*).

Yutkin used the radial spark drill shown in Fig. 8 to drill several rocks. This drill fires sparks along radii from a rotating center electrode to stationary electrodes around the periphery of the drill. In these tests, 4–5 cm diameter holes were drilled at rates ranging from

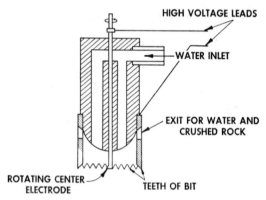

FIG. 8. Radial spark drill (Yutkin).

0.3 cm/min in diabase to 12 cm/min in clay (Table 10). The specific energy ranged from 95 joules/cm³ for shale to 340 joules/cm³ for marble.

Results of these spark drill tests indicate that specific energies of 300–500 joules/cm³ are required to drill sedimentary rocks such as

TABLE 10. *Radial Spark Drill Data.*[a]
(2 sparks/sec; 3 cm dia. drill; 4–5 cm dia. hole)

Rock	Charging voltage (kv)	Capacitance (μf)	Drilling rate (cm/min)	Spark energy (joules)	Specific energy (joules/cm^3)
Clay	25	0.2	12	62.5	39
Shale	25	0.2	5	62.5	95
Quartz	25	0.2	2	62.5	235
Marble	30	0.1	1	40	340
Diabase	30	0.1	0.3	40	1,130

[a] Ref.: Yutkin.

sandstone and limestone. This is about double the energy required by conventional drills (Table 3). Although spark drills require more energy than conventional drills, they have high potential drilling rates because they have potential power outputs of 100–200 h.p., as compared to 20–50 h.p. for large rotary drills.

Kulle and Ponomarev proposed the spark percussion drill (shown in Fig. 9) that applies a percussive load on a conventional bit. The sparks are discharged above a piston in a closed chamber containing a liquid with low electrical conductivity. Pressure pulses produced by the spark discharges are transmitted through the piston to the rock.

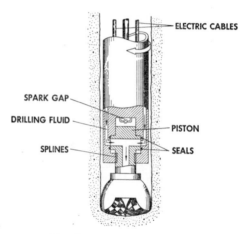

SPARK GAP

DRILLING FLUID

SPLINES

ELECTRIC CABLES

PISTON

SEALS

FIG. 9. Spark percussion drill.

Spark percussion drills require much longer duration sparks than the spark drills shown in Figs. 7 and 8. Optimum discharge frequency for this drill equals the natural frequency of the mobile system, while optimum spark duration equals half the reciprocal of this frequency. This differs from the other spark drills, for which the shortest and most powerful sparks are desired. The spark percussive drill has the advantage that the sparks are fired in a closed chamber in which the properties of the liquid can be accurately controlled for maximum electrical efficiency. Although no data are available, it appears that the Soviets have tested spark percussion drills.

Electrohydraulic Crushers

The intense pressure pulses produced by underwater spark discharges can also be used to crush rock effectively. Epshteyn *et al.* used the electrohydraulic rock crusher shown in Fig. 10 to crush shale, chert, and other rocks from $10 \times 7 \times 5$ cm pieces to fractions less than 0.5 cm. A 0.19 μf condenser charged to 40 kv was discharged at the rate of 5 pulses/sec, producing a power output of 0.76 h.p.

Titkov *et al.* used a similar electrohydraulic crusher operating at 50–60 kv to crush various rocks. A specific energy of 170 joules/cm³ was required to finely crush marl and limestone while 780 joules/cm³ was required to crush marble.

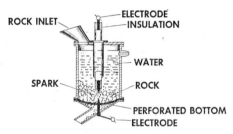

Fig. 10. Electrohydraulic crusher (Epshteyn *et al.*).

Bergstrom used an electrohydraulic crusher with capacitance ranging from 0.05 to 0.5 μf and voltage up to 80 kv. In these tests, the most efficient crushing occurred at 80 kv; at this voltage, a specific energy of 230 joules/cm³ was required to crush limestone to 0.1 cm size.

Maroudas and Taylor used a 0.005 μf condenser charged to 30 kv to crush various materials. Specific energies of 280 and 540 joules/cm³ were required to crush glass spheres and marble chips to 0.3 mm size, and an energy of 240 joules/cm³ was required to crush gravel to a 3 mm particle size.

These tests indicate that electrohydraulic crushers require a specific energy of about 100–500 joules/cm³ to crush sedimentary rocks, such as sandstone and limestone, to a 0.1 cm size. This is roughly 10 times the energy requirement for conventional crushing equipment (Table 2). Electrohydraulic crushers have the advantage that they can crush materials finely without contaminating them, in contrast to conventional crushers with which metal from the crushing elements contaminates the rock. Electrohydraulic crushers may therefore find initial application where sample purity is important.

Another application for these high-energy sparks is for splitting large boulders of rock produced by explosive blasting. Epshteyn *et al.* describe tests in which the electrohydraulic discharger shown in Fig. 11 was used to split large blocks of granite, limestone, and other rocks. The discharger was fired in a small borehole filled with water, producing high tensile stresses in the rock surrounding the hole. A 4.5 μf condenser charged to 65 kv was able to split 1 m³ blocks of granite and other rocks with one or more spark discharges.

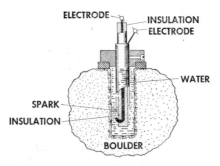

FIG. 11. Electrohydraulic rock splitter (Epshteyn *et al.*).

Breakage occurred without scattering of the fragments, thus eliminating one problem with secondary blasting. The specific energy required to split 1 m blocks of granite ranged from only 0.2 to 0.5 joules/cm³.

Explosive Drills

The Soviets (Ostrovskii) have used the explosive drill shown in Fig. 12 to drill over 3000 m of hole to depths of 4000 m. Table 11 gives the operating characteristics of this drill which pumps 3–12 explosive capsules to the hole bottom per minute.

A capsule contains two nonexplosive liquids separated by a membrane as shown in Fig. 13. As the capsule passes through a constriction near the bottom of the drill pipe, the membrane is broken and the liquids form an explosive mixture. As the capsule leaves the

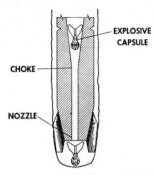

FIG. 12. Soviet explosive capsule drill (Ostrovskii).

nozzle, the fins spread apart; this frees a percussion pin that impacts and fires a detonator when the capsule strikes the rock.

The power output P of an explosive drill equals

$$P = 0.000022 \, nwe \quad \text{[h.p.]}, \tag{17}$$

where n = capsule pumping rate, capsules/min;
           w = weight of explosive per capsule, g/capsule;
           e = energy content of explosive, joules/g.

TABLE 11. *Soviet Explosive Capsule Drill Operating Characteristics.*[a]

Charge size	50 g
Charge energy	250,000 joules/capsule
Explosion rate	3–12 capsules/min
Hole advance	5–20 mm/explosion
Nozzle life	100–200 m
Nozzle standoff	20–40 cm
Average hole diameter	34 cm
Power output	17–66 h.p.

[a] Ref.: Ostrovskii.

Most high explosives yield about 5000 joules/g of explosive. The Soviets pumped a maximum of twelve 50 g capsules a minute, which corresponds to a maximum power output of 66 h.p.

This drill has produced drilling rates up to 15 m/hr and has drilled hard quartzite at higher overall drilling rates than conventional drills. While drilling, the nozzle standoff distance from the hole bottom must be maintained at 20–40 cm to make sure the capsules strike the center of the hole and prevent the explosions from damaging the nozzle. This standoff distance is maintained by periodically lowering the nozzle to the rock and lifting it. Considerable work is being done to develop hydro-acoustical and other automatic methods of controlling this standoff distance.

The capsules must remain in the nozzle for at least 1.5 sec to ensure good mixing of the liquid components. The shock wave from one exploding capsule can detonate another capsule in the nozzle, so it is necessary to space the capsules at least 1.5 sec apart at the hole bottom. Because of individual flow characteristics, the capsules travel at slightly different speeds in the fluid stream. At a depth of 1500 m, the travel time to the hole bottom varies ±1.5 sec, while in deep wells it varies up to ±4 sec. The explosion rate is therefore limited to

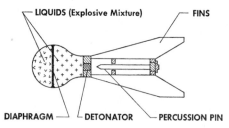

FIG. 13. Soviet explosive capsule (Raynal).

12 capsules a minute to a depth of 1500 m and 6 capsules a minute at depths below 1500 m.

There is little relationship between rock strength and explosive drilling rate, as shown by the laboratory data in Table 12. The explosions produced about equal penetration in granite and concrete even though the granite was 500–700 percent stronger.

Table 13 shows that hole depth does not have a significant effect on explosive drilling rate. The specific energy for drilling sandstone, limestone, and dolomite varied from 140 to 390 joules/cm^3, which is comparable to the specific energy for conventional rotary drills (Table 3). Clay has a detrimental effect on the explosive drilling rate because it yields plastically and is hard to remove from the hole bottom.

As the explosion rate is increased, the penetration per explosion decreases; this results in an increase in the specific energy (Table 14). It is more difficult to remove broken rock from the hole bottom at

TABLE 12. *Effect of Rock Strength on Explosive Drilling Rate.*[a]

Rock	Compressive strength (kg/cm²)	Hole diameter (mm)	Penetration per explosion (mm)
Limestone	130	57	5.2
Concrete	270	50	3.0
Limestone	370	42	2.8
Concrete	400	52	3.8
Sandstone	400	45	4.2
Marble	1400	80	1.5
Granite	1800	48	3.1

[a] Ref.: Ostrovskii.

TABLE 13. *Effect of Rock Type and Hole Depth on Explosive Drilling Rate.*[a]

Rock	Drilling interval (m)	Penetration per explosion (mm)	Specific energy (joules/cm³)
Limestone	0– 30	18	150
Limestone	560– 580	15	180
Limestone	615– 640	12	230
Limestone	1470–1540	9	310
Limestone	1515–1540	10	280
Limestone and dolomite	790– 850	19	140
Limestone and dolomite	1120–1160	14	200
Limestone and dolomite	1220–1250	10	280
Limestone and dolomite	1200–1430	11	250
Dolomite	1000–1200	8	350
Cherty limestone	625– 700	11	250
Cherty limestone	2040–2055	7	390
Sandstone and siltstone	1640–1650	19	140
Limestone and clay	2235–2290	5	550
Limestone and clay	2400–2770	4	680
Clay	2055	1	2800

[a] Ref.: Ostrovskii.

higher detonation rates, and this broken rock cushions the effect of subsequent explosions. It is interesting to note that in one drilling interval when the detonation rate was increased from 200 to 280 explosions per hour, the drilling rate in dolomite–limestone decreased from 2.6 to 2.4 m/hr.

TABLE 14. *Effect of Explosion Rate on Explosive Drilling Rate.*[a]

Rock	Drilling interval (m)	Explosion rate (exp/hr)	Penetration per explosion (mm)	Drilling rate (m/hr)	Specific energy (joules/cm³)
Limestone and dolomite	560– 580	180 288	15.0 13.6	2.7 3.9	183 202
Limestone	760–1000	360 720	17.0 14.8	6.1 10.6	161 185
Dolomite	1000–1200	318 570	8.7 7.0	2.8 4.0	316 392
Dolomite and limestone	1200–1430	200 280	12.8 8.7	2.6 2.4	215 316
Cherty limestone and clay	2400–2700	220 300	4.4 4.0	1.0 1.2	625 685

[a] Ref.: Ostrovskii.

This Soviet explosive capsule drill is of special interest because it has been thoroughly field tested and has shown that it can effectively drill holes at fast rates. This drill can penetrate nearly all types of rock and has the advantage of high power output. Its main limitations are that it will not effectively drill soft materials such as clay and that the cost of the explosive capsules is quite high since they are consumed at rates up to 720 capsules per hour.

The Soviets (Ostrovskii) have also developed a liquid explosive drill that automatically mixes the liquid components at the hole

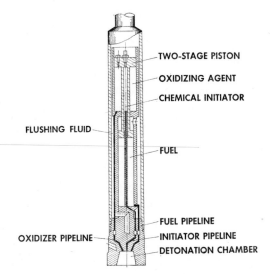

Fig. 14. Soviet liquid explosive drill (Ostrovskii).

bottom (Fig. 14). The differential fluid pressure created by the flushing fluid flowing through the drill acts on a two-stage piston; the piston forces fuel and an oxidizing agent into a chamber at the bottom of the drill, creating an explosive mixture. A chemical initiates the explosion. The correct timing of these fluid components is controlled by the form, cross-section, and disposition of the flow channels in the sprayer section of the drill.

The resulting explosion increases the pressure below the drill and interrupts the flow of the liquid components until the pressure again drops; the process then repeats cyclically. With different designs, the explosive charge can be varied from 3 to 20 g and the frequency of detonation from 150 to 2500 explosions a minute. The liquid explosive drill has higher power outputs than the capsule explosive drill (the capsules detonate a maximum of 600 g of explosive a minute, i.e. twelve 50 g capsules a minute).

Compositions of the liquid explosive mixtures are similar to those used in the capsules except that the choice of fuels and oxidizers is more limited since they come into direct contact with the flushing fluid. An alkali–metal eutectic alloy that reacts violently with water and the oxidizing agent initiates the uncased liquid explosives.

The Soviets have used uncased liquid explosive charges to drill 25–30 cm diameter holes by placing the explosives in the center of air-filled holes. These uncased explosives were considerably less effective than the explosive capsules.

Tests using the liquid explosive drill in a 200 m deep hole filled with circulating fluid were unsuccessful (Ostrovskii). Bottom-hole cleaning was a problem; the flushing fluid could not be directed at the hole bottom since it would dilute and wash away the explosive mixture prior to detonation. The flushing fluid was circulated some distance above the hole bottom, and as a result some of the broken rock remained at the hole bottom and cushioned the effect of the explosions. Another problem with this flushing technique is that when detonation failures occur, the explosives accumulate and subsequent explosions can destroy the drill.

If an effective liquid explosive drill can be developed, it would have the advantage of high power output. For example, a drill firing 10 g explosions at a rate of 500 a minute would have a power output of about 570 h.p. (eq. (17)). Means would have to be developed to supply the drill with 300 kg of explosives an hour. A technique would have to be developed to pump these explosives to the bottom of oil wells to prevent pulling the drill to the surface to reload it. This problem would not exist in mining or surface applications because of the relatively shallow holes.

The problem of flushing cuttings from the hole bottom and the inefficiency of uncased explosive charges appear to limit application of the liquid explosive drill.

Humble Oil & Refining Company (Robinson) has proposed an explosive drill that would use a sequence of shaped and gage charges as shown in Fig. 15. The shaped charges would produce long, narrow craters; the gage charges would blow these craters out to the desired hole gages. The charges would be detonated by differential fluid pressure acting across the explosive capsule as it passes from the bottom of the drill pipe.

Robinson made a series of tests using various shaped and gage charges in sandstone and limestone. Figure 16 shows craters produced in Indiana limestone at a fluid pressure of 105 kg/cm². As the

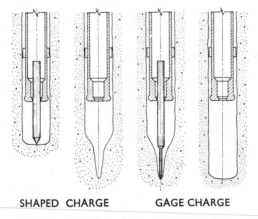

SHAPED CHARGE   GAGE CHARGE

FIG. 15. Humble explosive drill (Robinson).

fluid pressure on Berea sandstone was increased from 0 to 105 kg/cm², the length of the centers (1 cm diameter) produced by 17 g shaped charges increased from about 13–25 cm, and the total volume of the craters produced by the gage charges increased from 95 to 209 cm³.

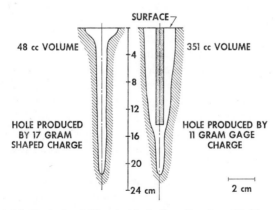

SURFACE

48 cc VOLUME   351 cc VOLUME

HOLE PRODUCED
BY 17 GRAM
SHAPED CHARGE

HOLE PRODUCED BY
11 GRAM GAGE
CHARGE

4
8
12
16
20
24 cm

2 cm

FIG. 16. Explosive drilling test in Indiana limestone (Robinson).

These tests showed that the gage charge is much more efficient than the shaped charge. For example, at a pressure of 105 kg/cm², the 17 g shaped charge produced a crater volume of 50 cm³, while the 11 g gauge charge crushed an additional 159 cm³ of rock. In this test the overall specific energy (shaped charge plus gage charge) was 670 joules/cm³, based on an energy release of 5000 joules/g of explosive. This is considerably higher than the 100–300 joules/cm³ required by conventional rotary drills (Table 3). With Indiana limestone, the shaped and gage charges crushed a total of 351 cm³ of rock, corresponding to an overall specific energy of 400 joules/cm³. The specific energy requirement for the gage charge in Indiana limestone was 180 joules/cm³, which is comparable to that for conventional drills.

In large-scale tests, 66 g shaped charges and 33 g gage charges were used on large blocks of Berea sandstone. The shaped charges produced craters about 13 cm deep with average diameters of about 3.7 cm and volumes of 60 cm³. At atmospheric pressure, the shaped and gage charges crushed a total of 1200 cm³ of rock for an overall specific energy of 410 joules/cm³. At a fluid pressure of 50 kg/cm², the explosives were more effective; they crushed 2800 cm³ of rock for an overall specific energy of 180 joules/cm³, which compares favorably with the energy requirement for conventional drills. Large-scale tests in a low-porosity limestone produced smaller craters and higher energy requirements. The explosive mechanism is apparently less effective in low-porosity rocks, because the rock cannot crush into its pore spaces.

Robinson reported that crushed rock surrounding the craters could easily be removed by scraping with a knife. With a field explosive drill, this crushed rock would be removed by subsequent explosions or by mechanical reaming.

The efficiency of explosive charges increases with fluid pressure, indicating that this explosive drill would be most effective in deep wells for which drilling costs are high. Efficiency also increases with explosive charge size, which suggests that a full-scale drill would be more efficient than the charges used in these preliminary tests. No attempt was made to optimize the explosive charges in the tests, so considerable improvement could be expected on a detailed development program.

These tests indicate that the specific energy requirement for the explosive drill is similar to that for rotary drills for nonporous rocks. Therefore unless means can be found to increase the efficiency of the shaped and gage charges, this explosive drill will require power outputs similar to the 20–50 h.p. outputs of oilfield rotary drills for comparable drilling rates. Based on an energy release of 5000 joules/g of explosive, a 20–50 h.p. explosive drill could require from 180 to 450 g of explosive a minute. In comparison, the Soviet explosive capsule drill has a maximum output of 68 h.p. when detonating twelve 50 g capsules per minute.

Erosion Drills

Considerable research is being done using high-pressure erosion jets to drill and excavate rock as shown in Fig. 17. These high-pressure water jets can drill the hardest rocks without the use of abrasives in the jet. Table 15 gives the operating characteristics of a four-nozzle erosion drill that drilled an 8 cm diameter hole in granite at a penetration rate of 15 cm/min.

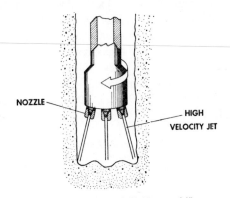

FIG. 17. Erosion drill (Ostrovskii).

TABLE 15. *Erosion Drill Operating Characteristics.*[a]

Number of nozzles	4
Nozzle diameter	1 mm
Fluid pressure	1000 atm
Jet velocity	440 m/sec
Hydraulic power	186 h.p.
Hole diameter	8 cm
Drilling rate (granite)	15 cm/min
Specific energy (granite)	11,000 joules/cm^3

[a] Ref.: Zelenin (27).

Pressures up to 5000 kg/cm² are used to produce jet velocities of 200–1000 m a second through 1–5 mm diameter nozzles. Neglecting friction losses, the power output P of these drills equals

$$P = 0.187\,naw^{-0.5}p^{1.5} \quad \text{[h.p.]} \tag{18}$$

and the jet velocity equals

$$v = 14.0\,(p/w)^{0.5} \quad \text{[m/sec]}, \tag{19}$$

where n = number of nozzles;
            a = nozzle cross-section area, cm²;
            w = fluid density, g/cm³;
            p = fluid pressure, kg/cm².

Equation (18) shows that the power output of an erosion drill increases with increasing nozzle diameter and fluid pressure and with decreasing fluid density. These erosion drills have very high power outputs and high potential drilling rates. For example, a drill using four 2 mm diameter nozzles at 4000 kg/cm² would have a power output of about 6000 h.p., which is more than 100 times the 20–50 h.p. which large rotary drills can transmit to the rock.

Farmer and Attewell used high-pressure erosion jets to drill various rocks. Figure 18 shows holes drilled in ferruginous sandstone using different nozzle diameters. Specific energies for the different rocks tested ranged from 17,000 to 38,000 joules/cm³, using a 1.59 cm diameter nozzle and a 500 m/sec jet velocity (Table 16).

TABLE 16. *High-pressure Erosion Drill Data.*[a]
(500 m/sec; 1.59 mm dia. nozzle; 125 kw)

Rock	Drilling rate (cm/sec)	Hole diameter (mm)	Specific energy (joules/cc)
Darley Dale sandstone	38	4.9	17,400
Oolitic limestone	41	4.1	23,200
Anhydrite	10	8.0	24,900
Carrara marble	16	5.1	38,000

[a] Ref.: Farmer and Attewell.

As the jet velocity through a 1.59 mm diameter nozzle was increased from 210 to 500 m/sec, the drilling rate increased from 3 to 38 cm/sec, and the hole diameter remained constant at 0.50 cm

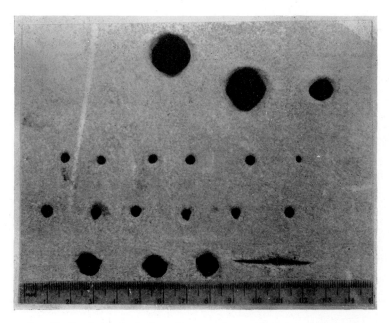
Fig. 18. Erosion holes in ferruginous sandstone (Farmer and Attewell).

TABLE 17. *Effect of Fluid Velocity on Erosion Drilling Rate.*[a]
(Darley Dale sandstone; 1.59 mm dia. nozzle; 0.50 cm dia. hole)

Fluid velocity (m/sec)	Flow rate (l./sec)	Drilling rate (cm/sec)	Power output (kw)	Specific energy (joules/cm^3)
210	0.42	3	9.3	15,800
255	0.51	7	16.6	12,100
300	0.59	14	27.0	9,900
340	0.68	18	39.3	11,200
390	0.77	24	59.3	12,600
435	0.87	30	82.3	14,000
500	0.99	38	125.0	16,800

[a] Ref.: Farmer and Attewell.

(Table 17). In these tests, the specific energy reached a minimum value of 9900 joules/cm^3 at a velocity of 300 m/sec, indicating that the highest velocity jets are not necessarily the most efficient.

As the nozzle diameter was increased from 1.19 to 4.76 mm (with the fluid velocity remaining nearly constant), the hole diameter increased from 0.28 to 2.8 cm and the drilling rate increased from 16 to 130 cm/sec (Table 18). These data show the very significant result that the specific energy decreased from 66,000 to 1500 joules/cm^3 as the nozzle diameter was increased from 1.19 to 4.76 mm. This indicates that the optimum nozzle size is larger than the 1–2 mm diameter used by most investigators. The larger jets are possibly more efficient because in large-diameter holes less power is lost in the interaction between the impinging and the returning fluid.

Leach and Walker used 5000 atm erosion jets (1 mm diameter nozzle) to drill 5 mm diameter holes in granite and other rocks at rates of 109–225 cm/sec (Table 19). The specific energy increased from 8600 to 17,900 joules/cm^3 as the compressive strength of the rocks increased from 330 to 1460 kg/cm^2.

Williamson and Parish describe tests in which 156 m/sec water jets were used to erode Berea sandstone (compressive strength = 570 kg/cm^2) under a simulated bottom-hole pressure of 35 atm. In these tests, 1.4 mm diameter nozzles at a standoff distance of 0.63 mm removed sandstone at the rate of 0.65 to 1.0 g/sec, which corresponds to a specific energy of 7700–11,800 joules/cm^3.

Epshteyn *et al.* describe tests in which Prof. A. N. Zelenin used the drill described in Table 15 to drill 8 cm diameter holes in granite at

TABLE 18. *Effect of Nozzle Diameter on Erosion Drilling Rate.*[a]
(Darley Dale Sandstone)

Nozzle diameter (mm)	Flow rate (l./sec)	Fluid velocity (m/sec)	Drilling rate (cm/sec)	Hole diameter (cm)	Power output (kw)	Specific energy (joules/cm³)
1.19	0.52	490	16	0.28	65	66,000
1.59	0.99	500	38	0.50	125	16,800
2.38	2.2	505	110	0.90	286	4,100
3.17	4.0	505	200	1.31	510	1,900
4.76	9.2	515	130	2.80	1220	1,500

[a] Ref.: Farmer and Attewell.

TABLE 19. *High-pressure Erosion Drilling Data.*[a]
(5000 atm; 990 m/sec; 1 mm dia. nozzle)

Rock	Compressive strength (kg/cm²)	Drilling rate (cm/sec)	Hole diameter (mm)	Specific energy (joules/cm³)
Red sandstone	330	225	5	8,600
Darley Dale sandstone	670	163	5	11,900
Carrara marble	1100	140	5	13,900
Aberdeen granite	1370	124	5	15,600
Pennant sandstone	1460	109	5	17,900

[a] Ref.: Leach and Walker.

instantaneous rates of 15 cm/min. This drill used four 1 mm diameter nozzles and operated at 1000 atm pressure to produce a power output of 186 h.p. A specific energy of 11,000 joules/cm³ was required to drill granite in these tests.

Voytsekhovskiy *et al.* drilled holes in concrete and limestone using water pulses consisting of 30 l. of water at a pressure of 65 kg/cm². These water jets (113 m/sec) drilled 4–6 cm diameter holes 2–3 cm deep in limestone and 16–18 cm deep in concrete. This corresponds to a specific energy of 710 joules/cm³ in concrete and 3900 joules/cm³ in limestone. In view of the tests by Farmer and Attewell it appears that these low-energy requirements were probably attained by using large nozzle diameters. Voytsekhovskiy also used water jets to split and crush large blocks of sandstone and limestone. A 1.3 m ×1.1 m × 0.7 m block of sandstone was split in half after 37 pulses. The failure mechanism in these large blocks of rock proceeds as follows: the first to third pulses drill a hole into the rock; the next three to five pulses deepen the hole and cracks begin to form; after four to five pulses, the high-pressure jets begin to penetrate into these cracks like hydraulic wedges, splitting the rock and forming cone-shaped funnels around the holes. The 30 l. water pulses each removed from 2000 to 2900 cm³ from limestone blocks, corresponding to a specific energy of 66 to 96 joules/cm³; this is comparable to that required by conventional crushers (Table 2).

Ostrovskii described tests where A. N. Zelenin used 1000 atm water jets (0.8–1 mm diameter nozzles) to cut slots in various rocks (Table 20). These jets traversed across the rock at a speed of 1.4 cm/sec and cut 3 to 5 mm wide slots ranging in depth from 1.7 to 9.7 cm. The

TABLE 20. *High-pressure Erosion Rock-cutting Data.*[a]
(2000 atm; 625 m/sec; 1 mm dia. nozzle)

Rock	Traverse speed (cm/sec)	Slot width (mm)	Slot depth (cm)	Power output (kw)	Average specific energy (joules/cm³)
Limestone	1.4	3–5	9.7	96	18,000
Marble	1.4	3–5	4.2	96	23,000
Granite	1.4	3–5	1.7	96	56,000

[a] Ref.: Zelenin (78).

specific energy required to cut these slots ranged from 18,000 joules/cm³ in limestone to 56,000 joules/cm³ in granite.

Browning *et al.* report tests where abrasives were introduced into the flame of a jet-piercing drill to produce an abrasion drill. Ordinary blasting sand is accelerated to extremely high velocities to produce an abrasion jet that effectively cuts rock. The advantage of this drill is that it mechanically removes the rock and thus can drill all types of rock, whereas the jet-piercing drill is limited to drilling spallable rocks such as taconite. A burner consuming 14,000 std. l/min of compressed air produced optimum drilling results when consuming 1–2 tons of abrasive an hour. These abrasive jets are 3–4 times more effective per unit air flow than ordinary sand-blasting techniques because the abrasive jets' energy per unit air flow is about 8 times greater.

The data presented in Tables 16–20 indicate that high-pressure erosion jets (1000–5000 kg/cm²) using 1–2 mm diameter nozzles require about 10,000 to 30,000 joules/cm³ to drill different rocks. The data obtained by Farmer and Attewell indicate that this energy requirement can possibly be reduced to 2000–5000 joules/cm³ by using 4–5 mm diameter nozzles. These latter values of specific energy are only 10–20 times greater than the 100–300 joules/cm³ required by conventional drills (Table 3), which indicates that erosion drills can probably drill faster than conventional drills since they have potential power outputs of 1000–2000 h.p. as compared to 20–40 h.p. for large rotary drills.

Ultrasonic Drills

Ultrasonic tools are used commercially to drill and machine diamonds, ceramics, and other hard alloys, and they can be used to drill rock as shown in Fig. 19. Ultrasonic drills use magnetostrictive or electrostrictive cores to vibrate emitters at frequencies of 20–30 kc/s. A magnetostrictive core consists of a nickel or permendur plate core with an electric winding through which a high-frequency current is passed. Under the action of the variable magnetic field, the core expands and contracts with an amplitude of several microns and a frequency equal to the current frequency. The amplitude of this vibration is amplified 10–100 times by using a resonant tapered horn between the magnetostrictive transducer and the cutting tool. The length of this horn plus the cutting tool is an exact multiple of the half-wave length of the frequency so that a system of standing waves is created in the horn. The energy is supplied to the larger end of the

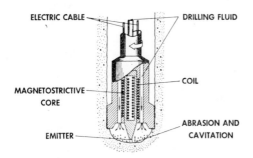

FIG. 19. Ultrasonic drill.

horn next to the transducer and is transmitted to the tool at the smaller end, thus magnifying the amplitude of vibration (which increases in proportion to the reduction in diameter).

The vibrating cutting tool removes rock by two mechanisms: cavitation and abrasion. In the water surrounding the emitter, cavities or bubbles form because of the transfer of energy from the emitter to the water. These cavities migrate toward the rock surface and collapse, forming high implosion pressures that microscopically crush the rock surface. Initially, the softer constituents are disintegrated; then microcracks develop around individual grains, and fragments spall from the surface. Cavitation dies out above pressures of 5–7 kg/cm², so this mechanism would not be important in deep-well drilling.

Hard abrasives (such as boron carbide or carborundum) are usually introduced below the tool, producing a suspension of abrasive particles around the cutting tool. Turbulence produced by cavitation draws many of the abrasive grains beneath the cutting tool, which impacts and accelerates them toward the rock at high velocity. The resulting high-speed impacts crush and remove the rock surface. High-speed movies made at the Acoustical Institute of the Academy of Sciences USSR established that this abrasive action is the primary cutting mechanism in ultrasonic drilling and that cavitation is relatively unimportant.

Neppiras (1959) found that the maximum cutting speed for ultrasonic drills is about 2 cm/min in soda glass, 0.4 cm/min in gem stones, and 0.1 cm/min in brittle steels and tungsten carbide (Table 21). The

TABLE 21. *Ultrasonic Drill Cutting Speeds in Brittle Materials.*[a]
(100 mesh boron carbide; 20 kc/s)

Material	Cutting speed (cm/min)
Soda glass	2.0
Flint stone	1.4
Slate	1.3
Garnet	1.2
Quartz crystal	1.2
Feldspar	1.0
Fused alumina	0.4
Synthetic sapphire	0.4
Synthetic ruby	0.4
Brittle steel	0.1
Tungsten carbide	0.1

[a] Ref.: Neppiras, 1959.

cutting speed depends on the type of abrasive used, as shown in Table 22. In soft materials such as soda glass, the different abrasives drill at similar rates, but in hard materials (tungsten carbide), hard abrasives such as boron carbide drill much faster than soft abrasives (sand). Ultrasonic drilling rate increases with increasing abrasive grain size, reaching a maximum when the grain size is slightly less than the peak-to-peak oscillation of the cutting tool (Table 23). The drilling speed also increases with increased amplitude of vibration, because maximum particle velocity and maximum impact momentum are proportional to this amplitude. Neppiras (1964) presents data which show that the cutting speed in glass (6 mm dia.; 20 kc/s)

TABLE 22. *Effect of Abrasive Type on Ultrasonic Cutting Speed.*[a]

Abrasive	Cutting speed (cm/min)	
	Soda glass	Tungsten carbide
Boron carbide (100-mesh)	2.0	0.082
Diamond powder (0.025 mm)	1.8	0.082
Silicon carbide (100-mesh)	1.6	0.051
Alumina (220-mesh)	1.3	0.004
Sand (0.30 mm)	0.9	0.004

[a] Ref.: Neppiras, 1959.

TABLE 23. *Effect of Abrasive Size on Ultrasonic Cutting Speed.*[a]
(Silicon carbide; 20 kc/s)

Ceramic	Cutting speed (cm/min)		
	100-mesh	400-mesh	600-mesh
Soda glass	1.6	0.7	0.13
Vulcanex	3.4	0.9	0.05
Z.Z. porcelain	1.5	0.5	0.05
Chemical porcelain	1.1	0.2	0.05
Frequentite	0.9	0.5	—
Temperadex	0.9	0.1	—
H.T. porcelain	0.8	0.4	—
Faradex	0.8	0.1	—

[a] Ref.: Neppiras, 1959.

increased from 0.1 to 0.9 mm/min as the peak-to-peak oscillation increased from 0.016 to 0.040 mm.

Neppiras also found that water is the best drilling fluid for ultrasonic drilling, producing rates 3 times higher than lubricating oils and 15 times higher than thin oils. Ultrasonic drilling rate passes through a maximum as the static load on the drill is increased, the optimum load increasing with the area of the cutting tool and ranging from about 0.1 to 5 kg.

Sviridov used a 200 w ultrasonic drill operating at 19.5 kc/s to drill various gem stones. Drilling rates of 0.4 to 2.5 mm/min were produced in 1.2 cm diameter holes (Table 24). This magnetostrictive drill was 40–50 percent efficient with much of the power being lost

TABLE 24. *Ultrasonic Drilling Rates.*[a]
(19.5 kc/s; 200 w)

Mineral	Drilling rate (mm/min)	Hole diameter (cm)	Specific[b] energy (joules/cm³)
Quartz	2.5	1.2	19,000
Jasper	2.5	1.2	19,000
Tourmaline	2.5	1.2	19,000
Agate	1.7	1.2	29,000
Nephrite	0.7	1.2	67,000
Sapphire	0.4	1.2	120,000

[a] Ref.: Sviridov.
[b] Based on 90 kw output power, since this drill was only 40–50 percent efficient.

to the water cooling the coil. Based on a power output of 90 w, the specific energy in these tests ranged from 19,000 to 120,000 joules/cm³, which is considerably higher than the 100–300 joules/cm³ required by conventional drills. This indicates that cavitation and abrasion are inefficient rock removal mechanisms, and that considerable power is lost to the water surrounding the vibrating cutting tool.

One of the largest current ultrasonic machines is a Soviet device that operates at 20 kc/s and has a 4 kw input rating (Neppiras, 1964). This tool can drill holes from 5 to 8 cm diameter in soft glass, removing a maximum of 10 cm³/min. This corresponds to a specific energy of 24,000 joules/cm³ based on input energy and 11,000 joules/cm³ based on output power, assuming 45 percent efficiency. These energy requirements are similar to those obtained by Sviridov.

Epshteyn *et al.* describe tests (at the Soviet Academy of Sciences) in which a 500 w ultrasonic drill operating at 20 kc/s drilled different rocks at rates of 2–4 mm/min. The 20 cm diameter drill used a 5 mm diameter cutting tool to cut holes with about 5.4 mm diameters. Based on 45 percent efficiency, the specific energy in these tests ranged from about 30,000–60,000 joules/cm³.

Neppiras (1967) states that the limiting lateral dimension of the ultrasonic cutting tool is about one-quarter wavelength of the horn that couples the transducer to the cutting tool. At the lowest ultrasonic frequency of 20 kc/s, the maximum cutting tool diameter is about 6.5 cm. As the size of the cutting tool is increased beyond 6.5 cm, the length of the coupler has to be increased, which in turn decreases the drill's frequency into the sonic range. An ultrasonic drill using a 20 cm diameter cutting tool could operate at a maximum frequency of only 6 kc/s, which would be audible, very annoying, and difficult to silence. This would be a problem in mining or tunneling, but would not be important in well-drilling. Neppiras states that a sonic drill could be easily made and would probably be more efficient than an ultrasonic drill. Although it would be difficult to drill large-diameter holes with a 20 cm diameter cutting tool, these large holes could be drilled by rotating a drill containing one or more ultrasonic transducers that cover only a portion of the hole bottom.

Available data indicate that ultrasonic drills require from 10,000 to 100,000 joules/cm^3 to drill different rocks. Because of their high energy requirement and low power output, these drills would be limited to very low drilling rates. For example, the largest current ultrasonic devices have power outputs of only 2 kw, which would correspond to a drilling rate of only 0.4 mm/min in a 20 cm diameter hole at a specific energy of 10,000 joules/cm^3. Because of low drilling rate, ultrasonic drills have little application for large-scale rock drilling at this time; their use appears to be limited to special applications unless techniques can be developed which will greatly increase their cutting efficiency.

Vozdvizhenskii and Skornyakov discuss the use of infrasonic oscillators of less than 16 c/s for drilling rock. At these low frequencies, wave amplitudes up to 5 cm in the drill pipe produce large impact forces. The emitters of these infrasonic devices usually act directly on conventional rock-cutting tools to make optimum use of these high impact forces.

CHAPTER 6

Methods of Drilling and Breaking Rock by Thermally Induced Stresses

THE drills that destroy rock by applying heat are divided into a group of drills which thermally spall and degrade rocks by heating them to 400–600°C and a group of drills which fuse rocks by heating them to 1000–2000°C. The fusion drills, which are described in the next chapter, can also be used to spall or degrade rocks (to do this, the power output of these drills is focused over a larger area of the rock to reduce the power concentration and prevent fusion from occurring). Thermal spalling drills are less versatile than fusion drills since many rocks will not spall, but they can produce high drilling rates in hard spallable rocks such as taconite. Although fusion drills are more versatile, they have limited application because the high energy requirement for fusing rock limits them to low drilling rates except in small-diameter holes.

Jet-piercing Drills

Although the jet-piercing drill was introduced in 1946, it is included in this study of novel devices because it is an exotic drill and it is the only new rock drilling technique that has found widespread application during the last 50 years. Most of the research that has been done on thermal rock breakage has been in relation to this drill.

The jet-piercing drill uses an oxygen–fuel oil flame with a velocity of 1800 m/sec and a temperature of 2400°C to heat and spall rock as shown in Fig. 20. Water cools the combustion chamber and the burning nozzles. This water also solidifies the molten rock and produces steam which assists in removing the rock debris. Operating characteristics of a jet-piercing drill are given in Table 25. Calaman and Rolseth found that although the stoichiometric ratio of fuel oil and oxygen is about 0.28 kg of fuel oil per kg of oxygen, maximum drilling rates in spallable rocks were obtained with richer mixtures having ratios of 0.33–0.36.

50

The jet-piercing drill burns 150 l. of fuel oil per hour, which would produce a power output of 2300 h.p. with complete combustion, based on a heat of combustion of 10,500 cal/g of fuel oil. Because of

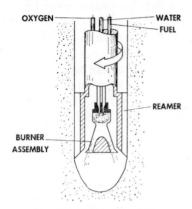

FIG. 20. Jet-piercing drill.

incomplete combustion and other losses, the effective power output in the flame ranges from about 500 to 1000 h.p. (Calaman and Rolseth). Power transmitted to the rock is much lower than this, because considerable heat is contained in the hot gases leaving the hole bottom (due to low heat transfer efficiency to the rock). A considerable

TABLE 25. *Jet-piercing Drill Operating Characteristics.*[a]

Hole diameter	16–32 cm
Drilling rate	3–12 m/hr
Oxygen consumption	28,000 std. l./hr at 10.5 kg/cm²
Fuel oil consumption	150 l./hr at 7.0 kg/cm²
Fuel oil–oxygen ratio	0.355 kg fuel oil/kg oxygen
Water consumption	3000–3800 l./hr at 4.2 kg/cm²
Flame temperature	2400°C
Flame velocity	1800 m/sec
Power output	Approx. 500–1000 h.p.

[a] Ref.: Rubow.

part of the output power is also used to heat and vaporize water at the hole bottom.

Typical jet-piercing drilling rates range from zero in many carbonate rocks such as limestone to over 12 m/hr in highly spallable rocks such as jasper and some taconites (Table 26). Specific energy

required to drill spallable rocks ranges from 30′
cm³, based on an output of 750 h.p. This is abo
than the 1500 joules/cm³ required to heat rocks to
ture of 400–600°C, which indicates that the jet-
15–50 percent efficient and transmits only about
rock. The remaining power is lost in vaporizing
duction to the borehole walls, or is contained
energy in the hot gases leaving the hole bottor
time between the high-velocity gases and the hol
to this low heat transfer efficiency. A detailed
balance for the jet-piercing drill would provide
into the mechanisms involved.

TABLE 26. *Typical Jet-piercing Drilling Rates.*[a]

Rock	Hole diameter (cm)	Drilling rate (m/hr)	Specific[b] energy (joules/cm³)
Limestone	25	0	No spalling
Shale	25	0.3	134,000
Dolomite	25	1.8	22,400
Slaty taconite	25	3.7	10,900
Syenite	25	5.5	7,300
Conglomerate	25	5.8	7,000
Granite	25	6.1	6,600
Sandstone	25	6.1	6,600
Magnetic taconite	25	7.6	5,300
Quartzite	25	9.2	4,400
Jasper	25	12.2	3,300

[a] Ref.: Calaman and Rolseth.
[b] Based on 750 h.p. output—only part of this is transmitted to rock at hole bottom.

The jet-piercing drill uses a relatively cheap source of energy and can transmit considerable power to the rock; consequently it should be considered for any application where it is desirable to rapidly heat rock on a large scale.

Browning *et al.* describe tests with jet-piercing channel cutters where the oxygen content of the gas was varied by mixing air and oxygen. The absolute rock removal rate was higher with pure oxygen because of higher power density, but the effective rock removal rate in terms of rock removed per unit oxygen required for complete combustion was about equal for pure oxygen and compressed air. A 50 percent oxygen flame was most effective, removing about twice as much rock per unit oxygen consumed. The optimum flame velocity in terms of effective rock removal rate decreased from 370 m/sec for pure oxygen to 240 m/sec for compressed air. Browning *et al.* explain that this reduction occurs because the nitrogen in the air increases the flame momentum. The difference in flame temperature and power density may also be contributing factors.

Forced-flame Drills

The forced-flame, or rocket exhaust, drill is similar to the jet-piercing drill except that nitric acid is used as the oxidizing agent for fuel oil instead of oxygen. The nitric acid produces a much faster reaction, resulting in higher power output than the jet-piercing drill.

TABLE 27. *Comparison of Jet-piercing and Forced-flame Drills.*[a]
(Iron quartzite)

	Jet-piercing	Forced-flame
Hole diameter (cm)	18	28
Drilling rate (m/hr)	5	18
Specific energy (joules/cm^3)	23,000	16,700
Combustion chamber pressure (kg/cm^2)	5–7	30
Fuel oil consumption (g/sec)	37	140
Fuel oil consumption (l./hr)	140	530
Oxygen consumption (g/sec)	103	—
Acid consumption (g/sec)	—	610
Water consumption (g/sec)	900	950

[a] Ref.: Shapir.

Shapir used the field model forced-flame drill described in Table 27 to drill iron quartzite. This drill consumed 530 l. of fuel oil and 2200 kg of nitric acid per hour. Shapir estimated a power output of 6500 h.p. for this drill, which corresponds to a heat of combustion of 8200 cal/g of fuel oil. Power transmitted to the rock at the hole bottom was considerably less than this (due to the inefficient transfer of heat from the high-speed flame to the rock as discussed in the previous section on jet-piercing drills). Because of the higher power output, the forced-flame drill penetrated iron quartzite nearly 4 times faster than the jet-piercing drill (Table 27). Specific energy for the forced-flame drill was about 30 percent lower, indicating that the nitric acid flame had a higher heat transfer efficiency to the rock than the oxygen flame, probably due to higher flame temperature.

Field drilling data for the forced-flame drill in iron quartzite are presented in Table 28. Hole diameters ranged from 27 to 35 cm, and maximum drilling rates ranged from 18 to 25 m/hr, except in one test where the rock was removed by fusion and the drilling rate dropped to 6.5 m/hr. Specific energy in these tests ranged from 15,500 to 19,700 joules/cm³ during spalling and 117,000 joules/cm³ during

TABLE 28. *Forced-flame Drilling Rates in Iron Quartzite.*[a]

Well number	Distance drilled (m)	Maximum drilling rate (m/hr)	Average drilling rate (m/hr)	Average hole diameter (mm)	Specific[b] energy (joules/cm³)
1	12.0	18	18	280	15,500
2	16.0	20	12.5	330	15,900
3	11.5	18	18	270	16,300
4	14.5	19	15	280	16,300
5	16.5	24.5	21.5	285	16,300
6	16.0	20	16	285	16,600
7	14.0	25	9.3	350	19,700
8	2.0	6.5	6.5	180	117,000[c]

[a] Ref.: Shapir.
[b] Based on Shapir's assumption of 6500 h.p. output. Only part of this power is transmitted to the rock.
[c] Rock removed by fusion.

fusion, which shows that fusion is a very inefficient method of removing rock. The specific energies in Table 28 are based on Shapir's assumption of a power output of 6500 h.p.; these energies are too high, since the short contact time between the hot gases and the rock resulted in less than 1000 h.p. being transmitted to the rock at the hole bottom. About 1500 joules/cm³ is required to heat rock to its spalling temperature of 400–600°C, which indicates that the forced-flame drill transmitted only about 500–600 h.p. to the rock at the hole bottom.

These tests have demonstrated that forced-flame drills can drill faster than jet-piercing drills, because of their higher power outputs. Despite their good performance, they are currently not economical because of the high cost of the nitric acid (which is consumed at the rate of 2200 kg/hr). The forced-flame drill is of special interest because it has demonstrated that it can drill spallable rocks faster than jet-piercing or rotary drills.

Electric Disintegration Drills

Sarapuu has used the electric disintegration drill shown in Fig. 21 to drill limestone, concrete, and other materials. This drill transmits high-voltage, low-frequency (60 c/sec) electric current into the rock through a sharp bit. This is accomplished by grounding one side of the generator to the rock. The bit is rotated at low speeds while air is circulated through the drill to remove the rock fragments and to create high temperature gradients in the rock. These temperature gradients create thermal stresses that break and spall the rock. Operating characteristics of an experimental electric disintegration drill are given in Table 29.

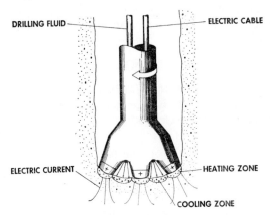

FIG. 21. Electric disintegration drill (Sarapuu).

The power P transmitted to rock by an electric disintegration drill varies as

$$P = kE^2/r \quad \text{[watts]}, \qquad (20)$$

where k = constant depending on the electrode
configuration, cm;
E = electrode potential, v;
r = rock resistivity, ohm-cm.

TABLE 29. *Electric Disintegration Drill Operating Characteristics.*[a]

Hole diameter	2.5–5.1 cm
Electrode potential	600–1100 v
Current	2–10 amp
Current frequency	60 c/sec
Power	1.2–11 kw
Power factor	0.93–1.06
Rotary speed	90 rev/min
Bit thrust	11–12 kg
Air flow	57 l./min
Drilling rate (concrete)	8–64 cm/min

[a] Ref.: Sarapuu.

Drilling rates are highest in rocks with low resistivity, because these rocks will accept more power from this drill. Rock resistivities range from 10^{-2} ohm-cm for magnetite to 10^{15} ohm-cm for quartz, which indicates that the penetration rate of electric disintegrating drills is very dependent on rock type.

The power P transmitted to an elemental volume of rock beneath the bit equals

$$P = i^2r \quad [w/cm^3], \qquad (21)$$

where i is the current density (amp/cm²). The current density decreases as the square of the radial distance from the electrode, so heating is greatest directly under the electrodes.

TABLE 30. *Electric Disintegration Drilling Rates in Concrete.*[a]

Bit diameter (cm)	Electrode potential (v)	Current (amp)	Power (kw)	Drilling rate (cm/min)	Specific energy (joules/cm³)
2.5	603	2.4	1.4	19	900
2.5	690	3.8	2.6	26	1220
2.5	890	5.6	5.1	38	1640
2.5	1040	7.8	8.1	47	2100
2.5	1080	9.2	10.1	64	1930
5.1	740	5.2	3.9	8	1430
5.1	860	8.0	6.9	15	1350
5.1	1000	10.0	10.2	19	1560

[a] Ref.: Sarapuu.

The experimental electric disintegration drill described in Table 29 was used to drill 2.5 and 5.1 cm diameter holes in concrete at rates up to 64 cm/min (Table 30). The power factor ranged from 0.93 to 1.06 in these tests, which shows that resistance heating was taking place. Dielectric heating was unimportant because of the low current frequency. The specific energy required to drill the concrete ranged from 900 to 2100 joules/cm³, which is considerably higher than the energy required by conventional drills. Tests in dense rocks such as taconite resulted in much lower drilling rates because it was necessary to fuse the rock, which is very inefficient and requires considerably more energy.

Field tests were made using power equipment capable of delivering up to 1200 kva. In drilling 12 cm diameter holes in limestone and topsoil, a maximum of 150 kva was used. Sarapuu reports that topsoil was drilled at faster rates than with conventional bits because of the drying effect of this process. Holes were also drilled in limestone, but the high resistivity of the limestone apparently resulted in low drilling rates.

The electric disintegration drill appears to be limited to drilling rocks with high electrical conductivity (such as iron ore) or for drilling porous rocks saturated with an electrolyte (such as water). Although the specific energy required to remove rock is greater for electric disintegration drills than for conventional drills, this drill has potential application for drilling highly conductive rocks because it has higher power outputs than conventional drills in these rocks.

Terra-Jetter Drills

Ross has patented a thermal drill, called the Terra-Jetter (Fig. 22), which would thermally break rock by cyclically heating and cooling it, using superheated steam and liquid nitrogen. Superheated steam (250–500°C; 40–60 kg/cm²) would heat the rock to about 300°C in 3 min and then liquid nitrogen (minus 196°C) would be sprayed against the heated rock to thermally shock and pulverize it. Low-pressure steam at 10–18 kg/cm² would then be circulated through two excavation lines to remove the pulverized rock from the hole bottom and to reheat the rock. This heating and cooling cycle would then be repeated.

The high-pressure steam would also assist in removing the rock by eroding it and by flashing water in the rock pore spaces into high pressure steam that would assist in breaking the rock. Phase changes and recrystallization produced by the temperature changes would also assist in pulverizing the rock.

Although no data are given, it is claimed that the Terra-Jetter drill would drill at rates up to 18 cm/min in medium-strength rocks and from 5 to 10 cm/min in the hardest granites. Since the heating cycle requires 3 min, this indicates that each heating and cooling cycle would advance the hole from 15 to 54 cm. It is doubtful that the effect of the thermal shock would penetrate this deeply into rock; therefore the drilling rates would probably be considerably less than 5–18

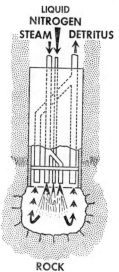

FIG. 22. Terra-Jetter drill (Ross).

cm/min. If the length of the heating–cooling cycle could be shortened significantly, the Terra-Jetter drill could possibly drill spallable rocks at high penetration rates.

High-frequency Electric Drills

Numerous laboratory and field tests have shown that high-frequency electric fields can be used to crush and break rock effectively. This technique could also be used to drill certain rocks as shown in Fig. 23.

These high-frequency electric fields heat rock by dielectric and resistance heating. Dielectric heating is produced by the "friction" between the dipoles switching back and forth; resistance heating is produced by current flowing through the rock. When high-voltage electrodes contact rock, dielectric and resistance heating occur simultaneously.

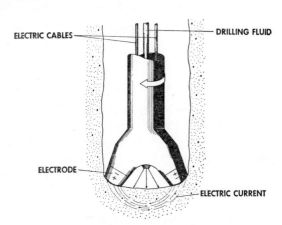

FIG. 23. High-frequency electric drill.

The dielectric heating power P_d evolved in rock is (Epshteyn *et al.*)

$$P_d = k_1 \epsilon \tan \psi \, E^2 f \quad [\text{w/cm}^3] \tag{22}$$

and the resistance heating power P_r is

$$P_r = k_2 E^2 / r, \tag{23}$$

where k_1, k_2 = constants depending on electrode configuration;
     ϵ = dielectric constant;
     $\psi = \pi/2 - \phi$ = loss angle, radians;
     ϕ = phase angle between voltage and current vectors, radians;
     r = rock resistivity, ohm-cm;
     E = electrode potential, v;
     f = current frequency, c/s.

Dielectric heating is proportional to the dielectric constant and the loss angle of the rock. The dielectric constants of most rocks are similar, ranging from about 5 to 15 (Table 31). Resistance heating is

TABLE 31. *Typical Dielectric Constants for Various Materials.*[a]

Material	Dielectric constant	Material	Dielectric constant
Vacuum	1	Marble	8
Lava	4–5	Limestone	8–12
Glass	4–6	Gneiss	8–15
Quartzite	7	Basalt	12
Mica	6–8	Hematite	25
Granite	7–9	Trap rock	19–40

[a] Ref.: Epshteyn *et al.*

inversely proportional to resistivity of the rock, which ranges from 10^{-2} ohm-cm for magnetite to 10^{16} ohm-cm for quartz (Table 32).

Both dielectric and resistance heating are proportional to the potential squared, so high voltages (1–10 kv) are used to break rock. Since dielectric heating is proportional to current frequency while resistance heating is independent of frequency, high frequencies are

TABLE 32. *Typical Rock Resistivities.*[a]

Rock	Resistivity (ohm-cm)
Magnetite	10^{-2}–10^{0}
Iron ore (50% Fe)	10^{2}
Dense limestone	10^{4}–10^{5}
Slate	10^{4}–10^{7}
Basalt	10^{5}–10^{7}
Granite	10^{5}–10^{9}
Calcite	10^{9}–10^{14}
Feldspar	10^{13}–10^{14}
Quartz	10^{14}–10^{16}

[a] Ref.: Epshteyn *et al.*

required only in rocks with high resistivity where dielectric heating predominates. Frequencies of 0.2–27 Mc/s are used in these devices, depending on the properties of the rock.

Kravchenko used 240 kc/s current to break blocks of iron quartzite weighing up to 10 tons into 3–8 pieces. The time required to break the rocks ranged from 1 to 3 min (Table 33). When the high-voltage electrodes were placed on the rocks, heating was initially slow until a conducting channel of hot rock formed between the electrodes after 1–10 sec. Following formation of this conducting channel, the current increased to 60–80 amp and the potential decreased to 300–500 v from an initial value of 1000–1200 v. As the current flowed through the conducting channel, the long, cylindrical zone of heated rock expanded until the rock fractured into several pieces. The specific energy required ranged from only 4 to 12 joules/cm^3, because the rock was broken into only a few large pieces.

TABLE 33. *High-frequency Current Destruction of Iron Quartzite.*[a]

Rock weight (metric tons)	Electrode spacing (cm)	Channel formation time (sec)	Fracture time (sec)	Total energy (kw-hr)	Average specific energy (joules/cm^3)
0– 0.5	30– 40	0– 1	5– 20	0.1–0.3	12
0.5– 1.5	50– 60	1– 5	30– 40	0.5–0.8	10
1.5– 5.0	60– 80	3– 7	30– 90	0.5–1.5	5
5.0–10.0	70–120	5–10	60–180	1.0–3.0	4

[a] Ref.: Kravchenko *et al.*

Young conducted similar tests on copper ore and granite, using a 50 kw radio station's output as a power supply. Voltages up to 9.2 kv and frequencies up to 27 Mc/s were used in these tests. The time required to break copper ore and granite blocks into small pieces ranged from 12 to 240 sec, and the specific energy ranged from 30 to 1570 joules/cm^3 over a wide range of frequencies and voltages (Table 34). These specific energies are based on input power and are high since the power supply was only 30–70 percent efficient. Specific energy requirements were higher in these tests than those by Kravchenko because the rocks were broken into smaller fragments.

Because of the conducting channel forming, Young found that the resistance between two electrodes on copper ore decreased from 200 to 0.5 megohms after 2 minutes' heating. The resistance returned to its 200 megohms in less than 2 sec after the current was turned off. Because of the large decrease in resistance, the resistance heating power increases rapidly as the conducting channel forms.

Since resistance heating predominates once the conducting channel forms, Kravchenko tested the circuit shown in Fig. 24; the circuit

TABLE 34. *High-frequency Current Rock Breakage.*[a]
(13–33 cm electrode spacing)

Rock	Frequency (Mc/s)	Voltage (kv)	Power (kw)	Breaking time (sec)	Specific[b] energy (joules/cm³)
Copper ore	5.0	7.2	7.5	20	70
No. 1	15.4	2.5	7.0	67	170
	17.0	—	38.5	45	390
Copper ore	0.3	7.8	22.5	240	450
No. 2	5.0	6.0	14.2	38	30
	15.4	4.5	15.0	23	60
	15.4	4.0	18.4	90	1570
	17.0	—	28.0	60	900
	27.0	—	4.0	240	280
Granite	0.3	9.2	42.0	140	170
	15.4	4.5	22.5	126	260
	17.0	—	9.0	12	30

[a] Ref.: Young.
[b] Based on input power to high-frequency power supply, which is only 30–70 percent efficient.

uses high-frequency current to heat the rock initially and form the conducting channel, and low-frequency current (50 c/s) once the conducting channel is formed. The advantage of this system is that low-frequency electricity is cheaper to generate. In this circuit, the

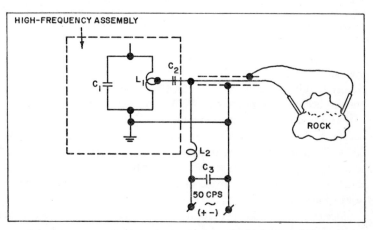

FIG. 24. Low- and high-frequency electric circuit (Kravchenko *et al.*).

capacitor C_2 and the choke L_2 isolate the low- and high-frequency circuits. Kravchenko in some tests also discharged capacitors into the rock once the conducting channel formed. This rapid influx of energy successfully shattered some rocks. In this capacitor discharge circuit (Fig. 25), a high-voltage transformer was used to charge a gang capacitor C_2 through the resistor R.

The relative importance of dielectric and resistance heating can be determined by considering a 1 cm cube of rock between two parallel electrodes. In this case, $k_1 = 5.55 \times 10^{-13}$ and $k_2 = 1.0$ [eqs. (22) and (23)]. With typical values of tan $\psi = 0.1$ and $\epsilon = 8$, a 5 kv, 10 Mc/s

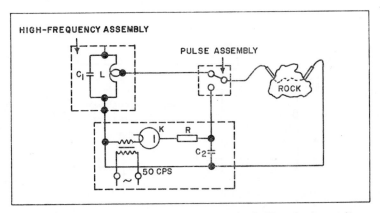

FIG. 25. High-frequency capacitor discharge circuit (Kravchenko *et al.*).

electric field would produce a dielectric heating power of about 0.11 kw/cm³ in both granite and iron ore, and a resistance heating power of 0.0025 kw/cm³ in granite ($r = 10^7$ ohm-cm) and 250 kw/cm³ in iron ore ($r = 10^2$ ohm-cm). This shows that dielectric heating is important in high-resistivity rocks such as granite and that resistance heating predominates in low-resistivity rocks such as iron ore.

Epshteyn *et al.* describes tests by A. V. Varzin, who used a 50 Mc/s, 6 kv electric field to heat and degrade rocks dielectrically in a parallel-plate condenser. After 60–80 seconds' heating, the uniaxial compressive strengths of these rocks were reduced by 50–75 percent (Table 35). As the rocks were heated, cracking sounds emanated from them prior to formation of cracks on the rock surface. Hard rocks such as granite or basalt were easier to break by dielectric heating

TABLE 35. *Degrading Rock by Dielectric Heating.*[a]
(60–80 sec; 50 Mc/s; 6 kv)

	Compressive strength (kg/cm²)	
Rock	Before exposure	After exposure
Sandstone	950	320– 520
Basalt	1600	470– 950
Granite	1800	440– 620
Chert	2800	680–1100

[a] Ref.: Varzin (27).

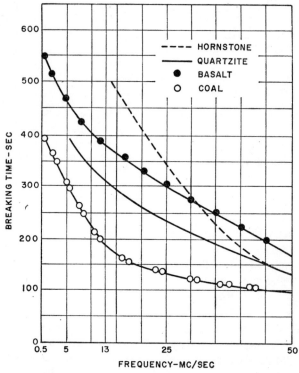

FIG. 26. Effect of current frequency on dielectric rock breakage
(Epshteyn *et al.*).

Fig. 27. Spalling oil shale by dielectric heating (Marovelli).

and often resulted in explosive failures. These tests also showed that rocks were easier to break underground (due to the stresses confining the rock). Specific energy required to break rocks dielectrically ranged from 19 joules/cm^3 for basalt to 112 joules/cm^3 for shale

TABLE 36. *Specific Energy Requirements for Degrading Rocks Dielectrically.*[a]

Rock	Compressive strength (kg/cm^2)	Specific energy (joules/cm^3)
Slate	800	72
Shale	900	112
Sandstone (fine grained)	1100	54
Marble	1400	36
Sandstone (coarse grained)	1400	38
Syenite	1400	86
Basalt	1600	19
Quartzite	2400	40
Chert	2600	32

[a] Ref.: Varzin (27).

(Table 36). The time required to break rocks by dielectric heating decreases rapidly as the current frequency increases, as shown in Fig. 26. Marovelli dielectrically heated and spalled oil shale, as shown in Fig. 27.

Microwave Drills

Rocks can be heated and broken by microwaves with frequencies of 1000–3000 Mc/s (Fig. 28). These microwaves are produced by magnetrons and are projected against the rock through waveguides. Dielectric losses, which are proportional to the frequency of the electromagnetic waves [eq. (22)], rapidly heat and break the rock. A distinction is made between microwave drills and high-frequency electric drills in this study because the microwave drills operate at much higher frequencies and dielectric heating predominates, whereas the high-frequency electric drills use electrodes that contact the rock, and resistance heating usually predominates once a conducting channel forms between the electrodes.

Steudel has made a detailed study of the mechanisms involved in heating and breaking rocks with microwaves. He used two magnetrons (2–2.5 kw) to produce 2400 Mc/s microwaves with a power output of 4.8 kw. These microwaves produced spalling on the surface of some rocks and fracturing throughout many blocks of rock. In sandstone blocks, thin spalls began to flake off the surface after 20–120 sec and fracturing began after 3–10 min, depending on the size of the block. Spalling continued as long as the rocks were subjected to the microwaves, forming crater-like depressions on the rock surfaces. In some rocks these spalls were only slightly separated, while in others they were thrown off the surface explosively.

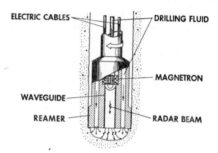

FIG. 28. Microwave drill.

As the rocks were heated by microwaves, cracking sounds emanated from within the rock and fractures began to appear on the surface. As heating continued, these fractures propagated through the rock. Although some of the blocks contained numerous fractures, they did not fall apart and mechanical work was required to split them. Sandstone blocks up to 1 m × 1 m × 0.5 m were broken after 5–15 minutes' exposure, requiring a specific energy of 3–9 joules/cm³. In tests on large rock surfaces, spalls up to 1 cm thick flaked off the surface but no fractures formed. The microwaves were more efficient when the emitter was placed in holes started by conventional drills.

In another test, a 40–50 cm thick sandstone block was heated for 5 min. The surface under the emitter reached a temperature of 300–380°C, while the opposite face was heated to 40–50°C. Steudel calculated that in this test 70 percent of the microwave energy was absorbed by the rock, 26 percent passed completely through the rock, and 4 percent was reflected from the rock surface. The efficiency is higher in thicker blocks, because less of the microwaves pass completely through the rock.

When slate was heated by microwaves, the surface under the emitter expanded outward and small pieces of rock were broken loose. This was apparently caused by the formation of high-pressure steam in the pore spaces within the slate. Quartzite, which contained no moisture, was heated only slightly after long exposure to microwaves.

Steudel found that the amount of microwave energy absorbed by the rocks increased from 7 to 70 cal/cm³ as the moisture content increased from 0 to 0.83 percent. When the moisture content was above 1 percent, the samples broke explosively after 20 seconds' exposure. These explosive failures were produced by high thermal stresses and by the formation of high-pressure steam in the pore spaces. As the moisture content increased from 0 to 0.2 percent, the dielectric constant increased from 4.6 to 4.8 and the tangent of the loss angle increased from 0.007 to 0.023. These tests have shown that microwave devices are effective for heating and breaking water-saturated rocks.

Steudel also heated desiccator-dried samples of sandstone, slate, quartzite, and other rocks; he found that the rate of heating was independent of mineralogical composition when the quartz content varied from about 2 to 82 percent.

Mullard Limited (Ironman) used two 5 kw magnetrons operating at 2450 Mc/s to break blocks of granite and basalt. The emitter was placed in 4–6 cm diameter holes ranging in depth from 15 to 50 cm. Half-ton blocks of rock were broken after 2–3 minutes' exposure, corresponding to a specific energy of 6–10 joules/cm³. These tests also showed that water-saturated rocks were easier to break than dry rocks. A concrete wall 150 cm high × 150 cm wide × 23 cm thick was shattered after two 3 min exposures (2 kw) requiring a specific energy of 1.4 joules/cm³. A 20 kw source operating at 915 Mc/s caused reinforced concrete to explode with sufficient force to separate the concrete from the reinforcing rods.

The Volvo Firm (Steudel) used two 5 kw magnetrons to break blocks of rock. These tests also showed that microwaves are most effective when used in holes started by conventional drills. Varzin (Ref. 27) used 1000–3000 Mc/s microwaves to break rock. In these tests, thin spalls flaked off the rock surface.

The application of microwave drills appears to be limited by low power output and low efficiency, especially in deep holes. Magnetrons

are only 30–60 percent efficient, so the overall efficiency for microwave drills is quite low. For shallow holes, the magnetrons could be
located at the hole entrance; in deep wells, the magnetrons would
have to be located at the hole bottom because the power transmission
efficiency in long wave guides is low. The limited space in these wells
would limit the power output of the magnetrons. Microwave drills
would have to be used in dry holes, because water at the hole
bottom would absorb or reflect most of the microwave energy. The
specific energy requirement for microwave devices would be on the
order of the 1500 joules/cm³ required to heat rocks to a spalling
temperature of 400–600°C. For this energy requirement, a 10 kw
microwave drill would drill a 20 cm diameter hole in highly spallable
rock at only 1.3 cm/min, assuming that all of the output power is
utilized. This is considerably slower than the 5–25 cm/min drilling
rate for jet-piercing drills in these rocks. The jet-piercing drills penetrate faster because they have power outputs of 500–1000 h.p. as
compared to 10–30 h.p. for microwave drills. Because of their higher
power output, jet-piercing drills appear better suited than microwave drills for drilling spallable rocks. The microwave drills would be
ineffective in drilling rocks which do not spall, since temperatures
sufficient to fuse the rock are not normally attained.

Induction Drills

When many hard rocks with high magnetic susceptibility are subjected to high-frequency magnetic fields, they are heated and broken
by induction heating. These rocks could possibly be drilled by an induction drill, as shown in Fig. 29. The magnetic field heats the rock
by remagnetization losses (hysteresis) and by inducing eddy currents
in the rock. In heterogeneous rocks, minerals with high magnetic
susceptibility are heated by the magnetic field while minerals with
low susceptibility are heated mainly by heat conduction. These rocks
are broken by the high thermal stress gradients and by differential
thermal expansion of the constituent minerals.

The hysteresis losses P_h vary approximately as (Epshteyn *et al.*)

$$P_h \propto B^2 f = \mu^2 H^2 f \tag{24}$$

and the eddy current losses P_e as

$$P_e \propto B^2 f^2/r = \mu^2 H^2 f^2/r, \tag{25}$$

where B = flux density;
             H = magnetizing force;
             μ = magnetic permeability;
             r = resistivity;
             f = current frequency.

Both hysteresis and eddy current losses occur simultaneously; which one predominates depends mainly on the rock's resistivity.

These equations show that both hysteresis losses and eddy current losses increase with the frequency of the magnetic field, so frequencies in excess of 200 kc/s are normally used for induction heating of rock. Eddy current heating varies inversely with resistivity and is therefore greatest in highly conductive rocks such as iron ore.

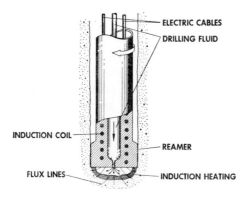

Fig. 29. Induction drill.

Both hysteresis and eddy current losses vary as the magnetic permeability squared and therefore increase with magnetic susceptibility k which is defined in the identity

$$\mu = 1 + 4\pi k. \tag{26}$$

In an electromagnetic system of units, k is a dimensionless parameter. For diamagnetic materials (repel magnets) $k < 0$ and for paramagnetic materials (attract magnets) $k > 0$. Table 37 shows that the magnetic susceptibility varies considerably for different rocks.

The magnetizing force for a coil with n turns varies as

$$H = 2\pi n I / R \quad \text{[oersteds]}, \tag{27}$$

where I = current through the coil, electrostatic units;
             R = radius of the coil, cm.

TABLE 37. *Magnetic Susceptibilities of Rocks.*[a]

Rock	Magnetic susceptibility (10^{-6} c.g.s.)
Clay	0–60
Granite	0–4500
Hematite	20–490
Limestone	0–25
Magnetite	640–135,000

[a] Ref.: Epshteyn *et al.*

This shows that both hysteresis and eddy current heating vary as the square of the current in the induction coil. For this reason, high currents are required for induction heating, resulting in large resistive power losses in the coil. This is one of the limitations of induction drills.

Gintsburg determined colorimetrically the quantity of heat liberated in iron quartzite by a magnetic field. Using eqs. (24) and (25), he determined that hysteresis losses predominated in iron quartzite ($r = 100$ ohm-cm) and that eddy current losses predominated in magnetite ($r = 0.01$ to 0.1 ohm-cm) due to its lower resistivity.

Kravchenko found that the resistivity of iron ore decreased from 200 to 5 ohm-cm as it was heated from 20° to 200°C. This decrease in resistivity would increase the eddy current losses fortyfold, which shows that eddy current losses become more important as rocks are heated. In some rocks, hysteresis losses may initially predominate until the rocks are heated and then eddy current losses become more important as the rock resistivity decreases. Heating reduces the magnetic susceptibility of a rock until at the Curie point it becomes nonmagnetic. Gintsburg found that it was not possible to heat magnetite above 500–600°C by induction heating because its Curie point is between 585° and 620°C.

Gintsburg used single coils to break cores of iron ore. With the single coil around the center of 10–40 cm long cores, the center 4–5 cm of the cores were heated to 200–300°C, creating high thermal stresses that broke the rock. Gintsburg also used a uniform magnetic field (100 oersteds, 240 kc/s) to heat 5–20 kg blocks of iron ore to a mean temperature of 300–450°C. In these tests, thermal degradation occurred at about 300–400°C. This uniform field initiated cracks in 5–7 kg blocks after 1 or 2 min and broke the blocks into three or four pieces after 4 or 8 min. A single 9 cm diameter coil (100–200 oersteds; 240 kc/s) placed above 20–30 kg blocks of iron quartzite initiated radial cracks beneath the coil after 36 sec. As heating progressed, these cracks spread through the blocks and broke them into three or four pieces after $1\frac{1}{2}$–5 min. In these tests a 50 kw generator transmitted only 7 kw to the rock, corresponding to an efficiency of only 14 percent. Most of the power was lost to the water cooling the induction coil.

Kravchenko also used a 9 cm diameter coil (100 oersteds; 240 kc/s) to break 5–540 kg blocks of iron quartzite (Table 38). The first cracks appeared after 7–90 sec, and the blocks broke into three or four pieces after 1–14 min. The specific energy ranged from

TABLE 38. *Fracturing Iron Quartzite by Induction Heating.*[a]
(9 cm dia. coil; 100 oersteds; 9–12 kv; 1–1.6 amp; 240 kc/s)

Rock weight (kg)	First fracture (sec)	3–4 pieces (sec)	Maximum temperature (°C)	Specific[b] energy (joules/cm³)
5– 10	7–35	50– 60	250–400	190
20– 45	30–90	70–180	200–500	90
200–540	30–90	90–840	240–300	50

[a] Ref.: Kravchenko.
[b] Based on 12.5 percent overall efficiency.

50 joules/cm³ for the large blocks to 190 joules/cm³ for the small blocks. Kravchenko stated that the power transmission efficiency was only 10–15 percent in these tests. Figure 30 shows the temperature gradients in a block of iron quartzite heated by a 9 cm diameter coil above the surface. The surface temperature was 240°C near the center of the coil and decreased to 50°C at a distance of 5 cm from the coil. The temperature directly beneath the coil dropped from 110°C at the surface to 55°C at a depth of 5 cm into the rock. This temperature gradient was measured along one of the produced fractures.

Kravchenko found that ore from another quarry absorbed more power and broke more easily. Three 100 kg blocks were broken into three or four pieces after $1\frac{1}{2}$–2 min heating, corresponding to a specific energy of 28 joules/cm³ (based on energy transmitted to the rock). An improved induction system broke a 1500 kg block in half after $1\frac{1}{2}$ min for a specific energy of 3 joules/cm³.

Rocks can also be broken by standing electromagnetic waves using reflecting screens, wave guides, or resonators (Gintsburg). An example of a reflecting screen is water under a layer of ice, the water acting as the reflecting screen. A wave guide can be made by completely enclosing the rock in copper sheath (except for one free face), while a resonator can be made by completely enclosing the rock in the copper sheath.

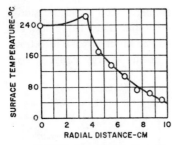 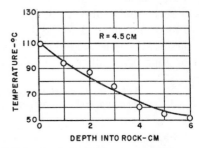

FIG. 30. Thermal gradients in iron quartzite during induction heating
(Kravchenko *et al.*).

The magnetic field equals zero at the nodes of the standing waves, so no heating takes place at these points. The magnetic field undergoes maximum oscillation at the antinodes, and maximum heating occurs at these points. Because of the uneven heating produced by these standing waves, high thermal stresses are created which break the rock. Gintsburg states that standing electromagnetic waves with frequencies of 10 Mc/s and above can be used to break unusually large lumps of iron ore (500–1000 kg) and also large lumps of nonmagnetic rocks. Induction drills appear to have limited application because of low drilling rates resulting from low power transmission to the rock. The low efficiencies of these devices and the fact that they can be used only in rocks with high magnetic susceptibility also limit their application.

CHAPTER 7

Methods of Drilling and Excavating Rock by Fusion and Vaporization

THE drills described in this chapter produce high-power concentrations capable of heating rocks above their fusion temperatures of 1000–2000°C. These fusion drills are versatile because they can fuse holes in any rock, but the high energy requirement of fusion limits them to relatively low drilling rates. Most of these fusion drills can also be used to thermally spall or degrade rock by focusing their power outputs over a larger area of the rock to reduce their power concentration.

Some of these fusion drills have already found commercial application. Electron beams, for example, are used to machine intricate electronic and optical parts, while lasers are used for drilling holes in diamond dies.

Electric Heater Drills

The Los Alamos Scientific Laboratories (Armstrong *et al.*) have used the electric heater drill shown in Fig. 31 to drill holes in basalt and granite. The operating characteristics of this drill are given in Table 39. This drill uses a tungsten or iridium resistance wire to heat the tip of the drill to 1200–1600°C. The resistance wire is surrounded by boron nitride, a good electrical insulator and an excellent heat conductor.

A downward thrust forces the molten rock up through a short tube in the center of the drill. As the molten rock extrudes from this tube, a high-velocity stream of helium gas solidifies it into small "popcorn"-like particles (having amorphous, glass-like structure) that are blown from the hole. Water is used to internally cool the sides of the drill to prevent the hot, viscous rock from sticking to it.

A 5 kw electric heater drilled a 5.1 cm diameter hole in basalt at 1.2 cm/min. This corresponds to a specific energy of 12,300 joules/cm³,

which is more than double the 5000 joules/cm³ required to heat
and fuse basalt (Table 1, p. 8). This indicates that over half of the
energy is either lost to the water cooling the bit or is conducted away
from the hole bottom. Another test, in which the drill was operated
at 2.25 kw (15 v; 150 amp), produced a drilling rate of 0.41 cm/min in
basalt, corresponding to a specific energy of 17,300 joules/cm³.

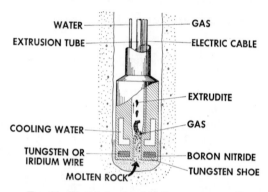

FIG. 31. Electric heater drill (Armstrong *et al.*).

Pollah and Skan (Ref. 43) developed an electric heater that drills
16.5 cm diameter holes in ice at penetration rates up to 15 cm/min.
This drill weighs 360 kg and is 7 m long. Suspended on a steel cable,
it is designed to drill to depths of 3700 m. It cuts 12 cm diameter
cores 3.1 m long, and it collects the melt water in a chamber located
above the bit. After each core is cut, the drill is pulled to the surface
to remove the core and melt water. The bore hole is filled with diesel
oil to prevent the walls from collapsing.

TABLE 39. *Electric Heater Drill Operating Characteristics.*[a]

Bit diameter	5.1 cm
Power output	5 kw
Cooling fluid	Water
Drilling fluid	Helium gas
Drilling fluid velocity	2000 cm/sec
Bit thrust	200–400 kg
Resistance wire	Tungsten or iridium
Drilling rate (basalt)	1.2 cm/min

[a] Ref.: Armstrong *et al.*

A diesel generator supplies 2300 v to the drill through 12 conductors in the steel cable. This is reduced to 230 v by a transformer in the drill for use in the heating unit. The power output of this drill is not given, but about 7.7 kw would be required to melt the annular ring at 15 cm/min. Because of heat conduction away from the hole bottom, the power output of the drill would have to be somewhat higher than this. If all of the ice in the hole were melted, a power output of 16.5 kw would be required, which shows that the power requirement is cut about in half by cutting the core.

Nuclear Drills

Nuclear reactors produce temperatures capable of fusing rock and could be used as drilling tools. Adams patented a needle-shaped nuclear penetrator (Fig. 32) for drilling through the earth's crust. The operating characteristics of this device are given in Table 40.

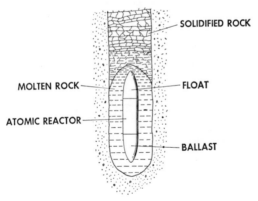

FIG. 32. Nuclear penetrator (Adams).

The penetrator would melt the rock beneath it, forming a bubble of molten rock through which it would sink. At a predetermined depth, a pressure release mechanism would drop the lower ballast section and reduce the density of the penetrator so that it could float back to the surface and melt the rock above it. The nuclear penetrator would contain sampling equipment and instruments for storing data and sending coded seismic signals to the surface. The penetration rate of this device would be limited by the rate at which heat could be conducted from the reactor to the rock.

TABLE 40. *Postulated Nuclear Penetrator.*[a]

Penetrator diameter	100 cm
Reactor	U-235 fission
Weight of U-235	100 kg
Fission efficiency	2 percent
Potential energy release	3.4×10^{13} cal
Temperature	1000–2000°C
Penetration speed	1–10 m/hr
Penetration depth	11 km
Penetration time	3–6 months

[a] Ref.: Adams.

A nuclear reactor could also be used in a more conventional manner as shown in Fig. 33. This drill could use a needle-shaped reactor
similar to the one proposed by Adams, but it would circulate gas or
water to solidify and remove the molten rock from the hole. This
technique has already been successfully tested in the electric heater
drills.

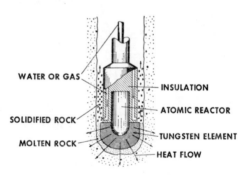

WATER OR GAS

INSULATION

SOLIDIFIED ROCK

ATOMIC REACTOR

MOLTEN ROCK

TUNGSTEN ELEMENT

HEAT FLOW

FIG. 33. Nuclear drill.

Power from nuclear reactors could probably be better utilized by
heating rocks to 300–600°C and degrading them so that they can
more easily be crushed or drilled by mechanical means. This could be
especially advantageous in hard rocks, such as granite, in which
mechanical cutters dull rapidly. This technique would possibly enable
driving tunnels in hard rocks with tunneling machines instead of by
the costly process of drilling and blasting.

In conclusion, nuclear reactors could be used to drill and crush
rocks by fusing and degrading them, but size limitations on these

reactors would preclude their use for drilling the small-diameter holes normally used in the mining and petroleum industries. Because of high cost and safety problems, it appears that nuclear reactors have little application for drilling or crushing rock except possibly on a very large scale.

Electric Arc Drills

Electric arcs produce temperatures of 5000–20,000°C and can fuse holes in any rock. Figure 34 shows an electric arc drill designed by Drilling Research Inc.; this drill rotates on rollers and has eight mud

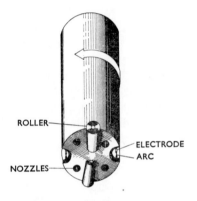

ROLLER

ELECTRODE

ARC

NOZZLES

FIG. 34. Electric arc drill (Drilling Research Inc.).

ducts for flushing away the spalled and fused rock. Alternating current would be rectified by rectifiers located above the drill to supply direct current to the arc. Operating characteristics of a 200 kw electric arc drill are given in Table 41.

Electric arcs are continuous discharges of electric current through a conducting gas between two electrodes. This gas is a high-temperature plasma consisting of electrons, positively charged ions, and neutral atoms. The electrons move toward the positively charged anode and represent most of the current since they have much smaller mass than the ions, which move toward the negative cathode. Electric arcs can be either "transferred" where the material being heated is used as one of the electrodes or "nontransferred" where both electrodes are part of the drill. Transferred arcs are not suitable

TABLE 41. *Electric Arc Drill Operating Characteristics.*[a]

Arc potential	200 v
Arc current	100 amp
Arc power	200 kw
Arc temperature	10,000°C
Arc gap	2.5 cm
Electrodes	Carbon
Arc environment	Gas or vapor
Arc consumption (atmospheric pressure)	0.6 cm/min
Arc consumption (500 kg/cm²)	23 cm/min

[a] Ref.: Drilling Research Inc.

for drilling most rocks because of their high electrical resistivities. High heat-transfer electric arcs can be produced by passing gases such as helium or argon between the electrodes at high velocity (6000 m/sec). This type of arc is discussed in the next section on plasma drills.

Electric arcs are similar to spark discharges except that they are continuous and produce no pressure pulses, whereas sparks are discontinuous and produce intense pressure pulses of 10,000–20,000 kg/cm². Electric arcs normally operate at 10–1000 v, whereas voltages of 10–100 kv are used to charge high-energy spark discharge capacitors.

Hydrostatic fluid pressure compresses an electric arc, increasing its power concentration and temperature. Drilling Research Inc. found that the potential required to maintain a 100 amp arc between two carbon electrodes (0.25 cm gap spacing) increased from 9.5 to 39 v as the hydrostatic pressure increased from 7 to 100 kg/cm². This produced a corresponding increase in power output and arc temperature which in turn increased the electrode burn-off rate from 0.6 to 4.8 cm/min. Extrapolating these data indicates that the burn-off rate would be about 23 cm/min at a pressure of 500 kg/cm², i.e. in a 5000 m. deep well filled with water. This high burn-off rate would limit application of the electric arc drill for deep well-drilling. Electrode burn-off is faster at the anode, because electrons strike the anode at high velocity and give up their energy to this electrode. The burn-off rate is high because the arc temperature is greater than the melting temperature of the carbon (3550°C) or tungsten (3370°C) electrodes.

Verte (Ref. 11) has proposed a drill that would use an electric arc between a center electrode and an incandescent shell (Fig. 35). This incandescent shell would be pushed through the rock, fusing the rock ahead of it. Solovev and Reksin (Ref. 11) proposed an arc drill consisting of coaxially positioned tubular and solid electrodes separated

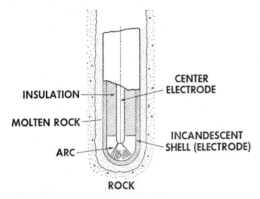

FIG. 35. Electric arc drill (Brichkin and Bolotov).

by insulators. Brichkin designed a similar drill in which one electrode was moved forward to maintain a constant arc gap as electrode burnoff occurred. Ledgerwood proposed combining an electric arc with a conventional roller bit, as shown in Fig. 36. This bit's arc would heat and degrade the rock, and the roller cutters would remove the weakened rock and cut the hole to gage.

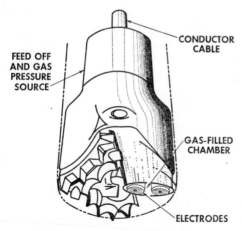

FIG. 36. Combination electric arc–roller cone drill (Ledgerwood).

Drilling Research Inc. used a 12 kw electric arc (40 v, 300 amp) to spall and fuse different rocks. In these tests, the arc was moved with a circular motion above the flat rock surface. Data from these tests are presented in Table 42. Craters ranging in size from 13.3 to 16.8 cm³ were spalled in sandstone, limestone, and flint after 6–15 sec, requiring a specific energy of 5400–11,200 joules/cm³ based on electrical power to the arc. This compares to 1500 joules/cm³ required to heat these rocks to a spalling temperature of 400–600°C, which indicates that only about 15–30 percent of the power was transmitted from the arc to the rock. The remaining power was lost in radiation, heating of the electrodes, heating of the air surrounding the arc, and heat conduction in the rock.

TABLE 42. *Crater Formation in Rock by Electric Arcs.*[a]

Rock	Mechanism	Time (sec)	Crater volume (cm³)	Specific energy (joules/cm³)
Flint (air)	Spalling	6	13.3	5,400
Limestone (air)	Spalling	15	16.8	10,700
Sandstone (air)	Spalling	15	16.1	11,200
Sandstone (water)	Fusion	120	14.4	100,000

[a] Ref.: Drilling Research Inc.

In one test sandstone was placed under water; no spalling occurred, and a crater with a volume of 14.4 cm³ was fused in the sandstone after 2 min. This required a specific energy of 100,000 joules/cm³ as compared to about 5000 joules/cm³ required to fuse sandstone; this indicates that most of the energy was lost to the water and that arc drilling would be very inefficient in a fluid-filled borehole.

Brichkin and Bolotov refer to work by Burlutskii *et al.*, who used electric arcs to crush blocks of rock. In their tests, 4 cm diameter holes were drilled 10–12 cm deep in the rock by conventional means; the arcs were placed in these holes 4–5 cm off bottom. After the rock began to fuse, the arcs were lowered to the bottom of the hole; the current then flowed through the molten rock, producing resistance heating and thermal stresses which broke the rock. The specific energy required to break sandstone, marble, and granite ranged from 2 to 32 joules/cm³, as shown in Table 43.

In conclusion, it appears that electric arc drills would be very inefficient in wet boreholes and that they would have to be used in

TABLE 43. *Breaking Rocks with Electric Arcs.*[a]

Rock	Rock volume (m³)	Failure time (min)	Total energy (kw-hr)	Specific energy (joules/cm³)
Sandstone (fine grained)	0.05	2.5	0.60	32
Granite porphyry	0.15	2.5	0.40	7
Marble	0.24	2.5	0.40	4
Sandstone (arkosic)	0.13	0.5	0.10	2

Ref.: Burlutskii *et al.*

air or some other gas. Even in air, the energy transmission efficiency from the arc to the rock is less than 50 percent. Based on input power to the electric arc, the specific energy required to remove rocks is about 5000 joules/cm³ by spalling and 100,000 joules/cm³ by fusion. Because of the high energy requirements, electric arc drills are limited to relatively low drilling rates except in highly spallable rocks.

Plasma Drills

Plasma generators produce ionized flames with temperatures up to 20,000°C; these flames can fuse holes in any rock (Thorpe). These

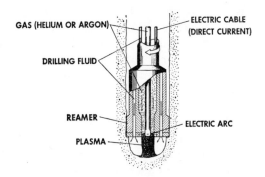

FIG. 37. Plasma drill.

plasmas are produced by passing electrical current through a high-velocity (200–8000 m/sec) gas flowing between two electrodes. This produces a high-velocity, high-momentum flame suitable for high heat-transfer applications such as drilling or weiding. Figure 37

shows a plasma drill suitable for drilling rock. Operating characteristics of a typical plasma are given in Table 44. These plasmas normally operate at potentials of 10–500 v and with currents of 100–
1000 amp. About 60–80 percent of the input power is transferred to
the flames, while the remaining power is lost to water cooling the
electrodes. It is necessary to cool the electrodes, because the plasma
temperature exceeds the 3000–3600°C melting temperature of the
electrodes.

TABLE 44. *Plasma Arc Drill Operating Characteristics.*[a]

Potential	300 v
Current	500 amp
Power output	105 kw
Electrical efficiency	70 percent
Heat transfer efficiency	Approx. 50 percent
Gas temperature	8000–12,000°C
Gas velocity	6000 m/sec
Gas pressure	10 kg/cm^2
Nitrogen or hydrogen	7000 std. l./hr
Cooling water	950 l./hr
Electrode life	50–100 hr

[a] Ref.: Thorpe.

Plasmas can also be produced by passing the gas through an
induction coil and subjecting it to a radiofrequency magnetic field
(Reed). These induction plasmas are low-velocity low heat-transfer
devices unsuitable for drilling. They are currently used for growing
crystals and other high-temperature applications where high heat
transfer is not required.

The plasma temperature depends on the type of gas used and the
amount of energy contained in the gas (Fig. 38). Diatomic gases such
as hydrogen and nitrogen can store considerable energy when heated,
so they are well suited for high heat-transfer applications. Because of
rapid electrode consumption, inert gases such as argon and helium
are often used.

Bouche constructed a plasma generator and used it to fuse and
spall various rocks. The power input to this plasma remained nearly
constant at 5 kw with potentials ranging from 14 to 36 v and currents
from 175 to 360 amp. Argon was circulated through the generator at
850 std. l./hr. This plasma was only 31 percent efficient, producing an

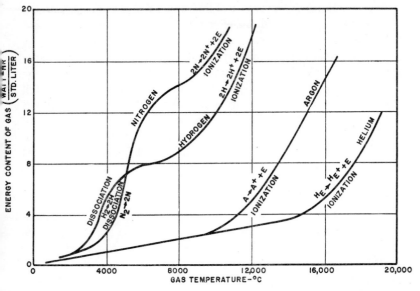

FIG. 38. Effect of energy content on plasma temperature (Thorpe).

output power of 1.55 kw. The remaining power was lost to the water cooling the electrodes. When the plasma was projected on a water-cooled copper plate, 65 percent of the output power was transferred to the plate while the remaining 35 percent was lost in radiation, heating air, and other losses. As a result, only about 20 percent of the input power was transferred to the copper plate.

The plasma flame was 7.5 cm long with a temperature in excess of 5000°C at the electrodes and decreasing to 1800°C at 2.5 cm from the electrodes. The energy content in the argon gas was 1.82 w-hr/std. l. (1.55 kw, 850 std. l./hr), which corresponds to a temperature of 7200°C as shown in Fig. 38.

The plasma was used to spall and fuse craters in marble, limestone, granite, and oil shale (Fig. 39). In these tests, the rock was placed 2.5 cm from the electrodes, so the plasma temperature was 1800°C at the rock surface and decreased as the plasma penetrated into the rock. The plasma affected only the surface of limestone and marble, decomposing the calcium carbonate to calcium oxide at 895°C. The flame temperature was too low to fuse the calcium oxide (which has a melting temperature of 2600°C), and this oxide formed a protective layer on the rock surface. Plasma-induced thermal stresses broke a

30 cm × 15 cm × 9 cm piece of limestone. The plasma also affected only the surface of oil shale, burning out the hydrocarbons and leaving ash on the surface.

The plasma was most effective in drilling granite in which a cone-shaped crater (5.1 cm diameter, 1.3 cm deep) formed in 60 sec by spalling and fusion. At a depth of 1.3 cm, the flame temperature fell below the spalling temperature of granite and cratering ceased. Based on a power output of 1.55 kw, this corresponds to a specific energy of 7700 joules/cm^3. The actual energy requirement should be about 2000–3000 joules/cm^3, since both spalling and fusion occurred and 1500 and 5000 joules/cm^3 are required to spall and fuse granite, respectively. This indicates that only 30–40 percent of the output power of the plasma was transferred to the rock as compared to 65 percent transferred to the water-cooled copper plate. Most commercial plasmas have higher temperatures, so the heat transfer efficiency would probably be higher with these more refined plasma generators.

Plasmas could also be used to degrade rock by heating it to 300–600°C, and mechanical means could be used to drill or excavate the degraded rock. In this case, the plasma would be focused over a larger area of the rock surface to reduce the power concentration and prevent fusion from occurring. This might be especially advantageous in hard rock where cutting tools dull rapidly.

Plasmas are ideally suited for transmitting large quantities of heat to the rock. They have the advantage that they are high-temperature, high-momentum devices with relatively high efficiency. They should be considered for any application where high heat transfer is desired.

Electron Beam Drills

Electron beams produce power concentrations up to 10^9 w/cm^2, sufficient to fuse holes in any rock. These devices are currently used for welding and refining metals and for machining precision electron and optical parts (Bakish). Electron beams have power outputs up to 450 kw and can be used to drill rock as shown in Fig. 40. Operating characteristics of a 10 kw electron beam are given in Table 45.

The electron beam is produced by a 5–150 kv potential that accelerates electrons from the cathode toward the anode. A bias grid along with electrostatic and electromagnetic lenses focus the electron beam against the rock. These electron beams are efficient, with up to

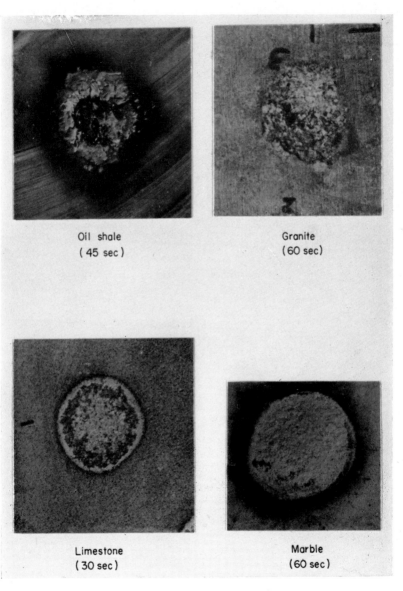

Oil shale
(45 sec)

Granite
(60 sec)

Limestone
(30 sec)

Marble
(60 sec)

Fɪɢ. 39. Craters produced by plasma drill (Bouche).

99 percent of the emitted current passing through the anode aperture. Tantalum and tungsten are often used as cathode materials because they have high electron emission and high melting temperatures.

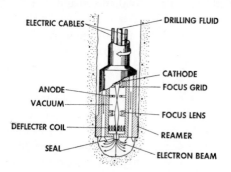

FIG. 40. Electron beam drill.

High-voltage electron beams produce better focus than low-voltage beams because there are fewer electrons in the beam to repel each other. At 30 kv the beam can be focused to 0.3 cm diameter; a 150 kv beam can be focused to less than 0.001 cm diameter. The high-voltage beams produce intense power concentrations and are useful for machining intricate electronic and optical parts.

TABLE 45. *Electron Beam Operating Characteristics.*[a]

Accelerating voltage	25 kv
Beam current	0.4 amp
Power output	10 kw
Beam focus	0.3 cm diameter
Power concentration	10^5 w/cm^2
Vacuum	10^{-4} mm Hg
Cathode metal	Tungsten carbide
Cathode temperature	2000°C

[a] Ref.: Bakish.

For electron beam rock-drilling, lower power concentrations are desired to prevent rock vaporizing and wasting energy. Therefore, potentials of less than 30 kv would be used, which would reduce the X-ray hazard and the shielding required.

Electron beams require vacuums of stronger than 10^{-4} mm of mercury to prevent gas molecules from scattering the electrons. In most applications, both the electron beam and the work piece are placed in this vacuum, but this would not be possible for drilling rocks, so a dynamic seal consisting of a series of differentially pumped chambers could be required (Williamson and Parish). As the electron beam emerges from the seal, the fluid or gas in the well bore would scatter the beam over a large area of the work surface. The electron beam could be electrostatically focused to sweep over the entire hole bottom by use of the focusing lenses, as is done when machining optical or electronic parts.

Electronic beams have demonstrated that they can drill holes in ruby crystals and other rock-like materials, but little information is available on the power transmission efficiency or the energy requirements. When drilling highly spallable rocks, it would be advantageous to spread the electron beam over a large area of the rock surface to reduce the power concentration and to heat the rock only to a spalling temperature of 400–600°C. This would require about 1500 joules/cm^3 energy as compared to 5000 joules/cm^3 for fusing most rocks. This shows that for constant power output, spalling could produce a drilling rate over three times faster than fusion. If the rock will not spall, the beam will have to be focused over a smaller area so that the rock will be heated to its melting temperature of 1000–2000°C. Care must be taken not to produce an excessive power concentration, or the beam will vaporize the rock and thus waste energy and reduce the drilling rate. For example, about 10,000–20,000 joules/cm^3 is required to heat and vaporize rock, which indicates that fusion drilling would be about two to four times faster than vaporization drilling for constant power output. In an actual drilling operation, both fusion and vaporization would probably occur simultaneously.

Drilling rates for an electron beam drill could be quite low when fusing or vaporizing rock. For example, a 100 kw electron beam drill utilizing 50 percent of its output power for fusing granite (5000 joules/cm^3) would drill a 20 cm diameter hole at only 1.9 cm/min. The drilling rate in a highly spallable rock such as taconite by a spalling mechanism (1500 joules/cm^3) would be 6.4 cm/min, which is comparable to rotary drilling rates in these hard rocks. The transmission efficiency may be lower than the 50 percent assumed in this example; lower efficiency would produce a corresponding decrease in drilling rate. Data on the power transmission efficiency of electron beams to rock during spalling and fusion are required before the potential of this drill can be accurately evaluated.

Laser Drills

Lasers produce coherent light beams that can be focused to produce power densities in excess of 10^{12} w/cm² (Groner). These power densities will fuse any solid and can be used to drill rock as shown in Fig. 41.

In the quantum concept of matter, atoms exist most of the time in one of a number of discrete, nonradiating energy states. Each of these states corresponds to a fixed quantity of energy. When an atom changes from one energy state to another, a photon of energy equal

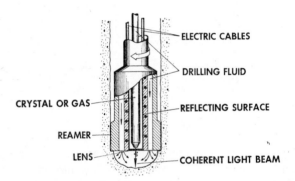

Fig. 41. Laser drill.

to the energy difference between these states is either absorbed or emitted, depending on the direction of the change. The energy E of a photon is proportional to the frequency f of the radiation.

$$E = hf, \tag{28}$$

where h is Planck's constant.

A laser beam is produced by exciting, or "pumping", a group of atoms to their higher energy states with electromagnetic energy and then dropping them to their lower energy states. As these atoms drop to their lower energy states, they give off photons of the same frequency and produce a coherent light beam.

Crystal lasers which usually use ruby crystals (chromium-doped aluminum oxide) are excited by intense bursts of light from flash tubes. Over 99 percent of the pumping energy is lost to the cooling fluid; consequently, these lasers can be used only in brief bursts to allow dissipation of this heat. The crystals are accurately machined and the ends are silvered so that they act as resonance cavities to amplify the radiation. Operating characteristics of one of the largest current crystal lasers are given in Table 46. This laser produces 100 joule bursts lasting 1 msec every 2 sec. This corresponds to an instantaneous power output of 10^5 w and an average power output of only 50 w.

TABLE 46. *Ruby Crystal Laser Operating Characteristics.*[a]

Efficiency	0.1–1 percent
Wavelength	0.69 micron
Pulse rate	30 pulses/min
Pulse duration	1 msec
Pulse energy	100 joules
Instantaneous power	100 kw
Average power	50 w
Theoretical focus	0.01 micron^2
Actual focus	100 micron^2
Actual power density	10^{11} w/cm^2

[a] Ref.: Friedlander.

Gas lasers that use mixtures of gases to produce different energy levels can be pumped by electron beams, thus allowing continuous laser operation. Collisions between the electrons and atoms excite the atoms to their higher energy states when the kinetic energy of the electrons corresponds to the energy difference between the energy states. These gas lasers can be pumped continuously by glow discharges from a discharge tube subjected to radiofrequency energy or

TABLE 47. *Gas Laser Operating Characteristics.*[a]

Gas	N_2–CO_2–He
Gas flow rate	2830 l./min
Cooling fluid	Water
Discharge tube length	13.4 m
Wavelength	10.6 microns
Beam divergence	2 milliradians
Beam diameter	4.4 cm
Actual focus	500 micron^2
Power output	1000 w
Power concentration	2×10^8 w/cm^2
Efficiency	15 percent

[a] Ref.: *Scientific Research* (42).

by a d.c.-excited electron beam. Operating characteristics of a 15 percent efficient, 1 kw continuous gas laser are given in Table 47. This d.c.-excited laser uses a mixture of nitrogen, carbon dioxide, and helium flowing at 2830 l./min.

When a laser beam is focused on a rock or other material, there is an initial transient period followed by a steady-state condition in which the volumetric rock removal rate is constant and the bottom of the hole is covered by a layer of molten rock. For devices with high-power density, such as lasers or electron beams, the temperature distribution into the rock is closely approximated by the distribution for a uniformly heated surface (Adams and Hardway):

$$\frac{T - T_o}{T_m - T_o} = e^{-Rx/K}, \tag{29}$$

where
$T =$ temperature at distance x below surface, °C;
$T_o =$ initial temperature of rock, °C;
$T_m =$ melting temperature, °C;
$x =$ distance below surface, cm;
$R =$ penetration rate, cm/min;
$K =$ thermal diffusivity, i.e. $k/\rho c$ (cm²/sec);
$k =$ thermal conductivity, cal/cm sec °C;
$\rho =$ density, g/cm³;
$c =$ specific heat, cal/g °C.

Equation (29) shows that the higher the penetration rate (i.e. the higher the power density), the steeper the temperature gradient into the rock. Because of their high-power densities, this temperature gradient is very steep for lasers and electron beams. For example, when drilling a typical granite ($T_m = 1100$°C, $K = 0.012$ cm²/sec, $T_o = 20$°C) at 10 cm/min, the temperature decreases from 1100°C at the surface of the rock to 75°C at a distance $x = 2.2$ mm below the surface. With these high-power densities, heat conduction away from the hole bottom is not a major problem; most of the energy transmitted to the hole bottom will be used in fusing the rock. With devices having lower power densities, such as induction or microwave drills, heat conduction away from the hole bottom is more important.

Lasers can also be used to drill some rocks by a spalling mechanism. In this case, the laser would be focused over a larger area of the rock surface to heat the rock to a spalling temperature of 400–600°C instead of to a fusing temperature of 1000–2000°C. Less energy would be reflected away from the hole bottom due to the lower power density.

Although many rocks will not spall, some of them can be degraded and weakened by heating them to 300–600°C using lasers. Thermal stresses produced by high-temperature gradients and differential thermal expansion of the constituent minerals weaken and break the bonds between the crystals and grains.

Gladstone and Kettaneh used the 1 kw gas laser described in Table 47 to heat and degrade granite, marble, gneiss, and schist. The laser beam was used in an unfocused manner to heat the rock over a 3.8 cm diameter area. Very little energy was reflected from the rock surface in these tests. These rocks were heated until they glowed with an intense white light. After 3–5 seconds' exposure, cracks began to appear in the rocks; after 30 seconds' exposure, the rocks had experienced considerable reduction in strength. These results are similar to the 50–75 percent reductions in strength for rocks heated dielectrically between two condenser plates by Varzin (Table 35). About 1000–1500 joules/cm³ is required to heat these rocks to 300–600°C and degrade them in this manner.

Because of low power output, it appears that lasers are currently limited to low drilling rates except in small-diameter holes. The 1 kw gas laser described in Table 47 is one of the largest current lasers. If the total output power of this laser were utilized, it would fuse (5000 joules/cm³) a 1 mm diameter hole at 1500 cm/min and a 20 cm diameter hole at only 0.04 cm/min. This compares unfavorably to drilling rates of 2–100 cm/min for conventional drills. In spallable rocks (1500 joules/cm³), the rates would be 5100 cm/min in a 1 mm diameter hole, and only 0.1 cm/min in a 20 cm diameter hole as compared to 10–20 cm/min for conventional jet-piercing drills. This indicates that the power output of lasers will have to be increased by at least two orders of magnitude before they can produce penetration rates comparable to conventional drills in larger diameter holes. Lasers can currently drill small-diameter holes faster than conventional drills can.

Lasers could also be used to fuse slots, or "kerfs", at the hole bottom or in a tunnel wall to allow easy breakage or removal of large pieces of rock by mechanical methods. This could greatly reduce the amount of power required and thus increase the penetration rate. For example, cutting a 1 mm wide slot around a 20 cm diameter core would require less than 1 percent of the energy required to fuse the entire core of rock. In this case, the 1 kw laser would drill a 20 cm diameter hole at 6 cm/min by fusion and 20 cm/min by spalling, assuming that all of the output power were utilized. These rates are comparable to those for conventional drills. Mechanical power required to crush an unsupported core would be low, because it is much easier to crush rock than to drill it because of the additional free surfaces (Table 2, p. 10). For example, only 1.8 h.p. mechanical power would be required to crush the core (40 joules/cm³) when drilling at 6 cm/min, and 5.7 h.p. at 20 cm/min. Because of the low mechanical power required, it should be easy to mechanically crush this core as fast as the laser can produce it. A similar method could be used on a tunnel face using intersecting sets of slots.

Because of low power output, it appears that lasers are currently limited to drilling small holes or for use in conjunction with mechanical methods where the laser is used to degrade or cut slots in the rock. If the output power of lasers can be increased by two or more orders of magnitude, they may find application for large-scale rock breakage.

CHAPTER 8

Chemical Methods of Drilling and Excavating Rock

CHEMICAL drills (Refs. 69 and 95) have been successfully used to drill sandstone, limestone, and granite in the laboratory. These drills use fluorine and other reactive chemicals to produce high-speed reactions that remove the rock. These reactions, which are of sufficient intensity to set fire to asbestos, produce harmless products which are blown from the hole.

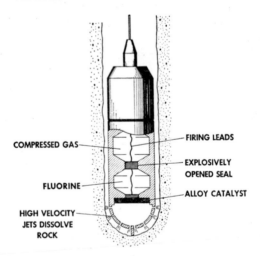

FIG. 42. Chemical drill (Ledgerwood).

A chemical drill could be used on a wireline, as shown in Fig. 42. An electric detonator would be used to break a seal between a chamber of compressed gas and a chamber containing the reactive chemical. The compressed gas would force the fluorine or other chemical through a catalyst, producing a high-velocity chemical jet that dissolves the rock. The tool would then be lifted to the surface,

92

recharged, and the process repeated. The chemical drill appears to have little application for large-scale rock drilling because of high chemical costs and because of the difficulty in handling large volumes of highly reactive chemicals.

CHAPTER 9

Critique of Novel Drilling Methods

BEFORE the potential of a new drilling device can be evaluated, it is necessary to know its approximate drilling rate. The maximum drilling rate is controlled by the amount of power that can be delivered to the rock, and deliverable power is limited by either the power transmission down the bore-hole, by the power output of the drill, or by the power the rock will accept from the drill.

The following drills are limited primarily by the amount of power that can be delivered down the borehole:

1. Chemical
2. Erosion
3. Explosive
4. Implosion
5. Pellet
6. Turbine

These drills utilize as much power as can be delivered to them, so their drilling rates are proportional to the power delivered down the drill pipe. The drilling rate of the chemical drill is limited by the rate at which chemicals can be delivered to the hole bottom. Research on the erosion, explosive, and implosion drills should be aimed primarily at delivering more power to the hole bottom and at reducing the specific energy requirement for rock removal. Research on the pellet and turbine drills should be directed toward increasing the efficiency of these tools, since only 4–20 percent of the hydraulic power is converted to mechanical power and transmitted to the rock.

The following drills are limited primarily by their power outputs:

1. Conventional percussive
2. Electric arc
3. Electron beam
4. Forced-flame
5. Jet-piercing
6. Laser
7. Plasma
8. Spark
9. Spark-percussive
10. Ultrasonic

Drilling rates of these drills are proportional to their power outputs, so research should be aimed primarily at increasing their power outputs and at reducing the specific energy required for rock removal.

The following drills are limited by the amount of power the rocks will accept from the drills:

1. Conventional rotary
2. Electric disintegration
3. Terra-Jetter
4. High-frequency electric
5. Induction
6. Nuclear

Research on this group of drills should be aimed primarily at increasing the rate at which rock will accept energy from the drill and at reducing the specific energy required to remove the rock. In highly conductive rocks such as magnetite, the rock will accept all of the power which can be delivered to it by the electric disintegration drill, in which case the drilling rate will be limited by power transmission down the borehole.

The maximum drilling rate for each of the novel drills is estimated in Table 48 for a 20 cm diameter hole in medium-strength rock. The specific energy and power output are estimated for each of the drills, based on available data presented in Chapters 5–7 and on the operating characteristics of commercially available equipment. Considerations used in making these estimates of specific energies and power outputs are discussed in more detail in Appendix 1. As new equipment and techniques are developed, the reader can easily revise the values of specific energy and power output in Table 48 and use eq. (8) to recalculate the maximum potential drilling rate.

For a 20 cm diameter hole, eq. (8) reduces to

$$R = 141\, P/E \quad \text{[cm/min]}, \tag{30}$$

where P = power transmitted to rock, h.p.;

E = specific energy, joules/cm^3.

Figure 43 is a nomograph relating drilling rate, power output, specific energy and hole diameter [eq. (8)]. For the example shown, a 100 h.p. drill operating at a specific energy of 10,000 joules/cm^3 would drill a 10 cm diameter hole at 5.6 cm/min.

Table 48 shows that the spark, erosion, and explosive drills can drill faster than conventional drills in some rocks. These three drills are versatile, since they remove rock mechanically and can drill any type of rock. Forced-flame and jet-piercing drills can also drill faster than conventional drills in hard, spallable rocks such as taconite, but they are not as versatile since they remove rock by a spalling mechanism and many rocks will not spall. Electrode consumption and capacitor life are important factors to consider when evaluating

TABLE 48. *Estimates of Maximum Drilling Rates for 20 cm Diameter Novel Drills in Medium-strength Rock.*

Drill	Status	Rock Removal Mechanism	Specific energy (joules/cm³)	Maximum power to rock (h.p.)	Maximum potential drilling rate (cm/min)
Rotary[a]	Field drill	Mechanical	200–500	20–30	14–85
Spark[a]	Laboratory drill	Mechanical	200–400	100–200	35–140
Erosion[a]	Laboratory drill	Mechanical	2000–4000	1000–2000	35–140
Explosive[a]	Field drill	Mechanical	200–400	75–100	26–70
Forced-flame	Field drill	Spalling[b]	1500	300–600	28–56
Jet-piercing	Field drill	Spalling[b]	1500	100–200	9–18
Electric disintegration	Laboratory drill	Spalling[c]	1500	100–150	9–14
Pellet[a]	Laboratory drill	Mechanical[a]	200–400	10–20	4–14
Turbine[a]	Field drill	Mechanical[a]	400–1300	30–40	3–14
Plasma	Laboratory tests	Spalling[b]	1500	80–120	8–11
Electric arc	Laboratory tests	Spalling[b]	1500	45–90	4–8
High-frequency	Shatters rocks	Spalling[b]	1500	30–60	3–6
Plasma	Laboratory tests	Fusion	5000	80–120	2–3
Electric heater	Laboratory drill	Fusion	5000	50–100	1–3
Electric arc	Laboratory tests	Fusion	5000	45–90	1–3
Nuclear	Conceptual	Fusion	5000	1250–2500[e]	1–3
Laser	Small holes	Spalling	1500	12–24	1–2
Electron beam	Small holes	Spalling[b]	1500	10–20	1–2
Microwave	Shatters rock	Spalling[b]	1500	10–20	1–2
Induction	Shatters rock	Spalling[d]	1500	5–10	0.5–1.0
Laser	Small holes	Fusion	5000	10–20	0.3–0.6
Electron beam	Small holes	Fusion	5000	10–20	0.3–0.6
Electron beam	Small holes	Vaporization	12,000	10–20	0.1–0.2
Laser	Small holes	Vaporization	12,000	7–14	0.1–0.2
Ultrasonic[a]	Laboratory drill	Mechanical	20,000	5–10	0.04–0.07

[a] Water-filled borehole.
[b] Limited to highly spallable rock such as taconite.
[c] Limited to highly spallable rock with high electrical conductivity.
[d] Limited to highly spallable rock with high magnetic susceptibility.
[e] 100 cm diameter drill.

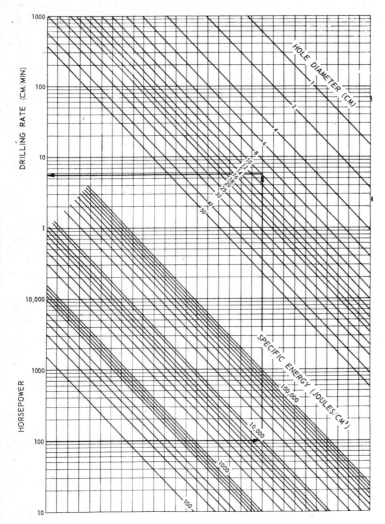

FIG. 43. Drilling rate nomograph.

the economic potential of spark drills. The explosive capsule cost is an important item with explosive drills, since up to 720 capsules are used an hour. Erosion drills can drill at very high rates, but nozzle erosion may be a problem and will limit the time which this drill can remain at the hole bottom. Erosion drills require high power outputs, thus necessitating the development of large-capacity, high-pressure pumps. Because of their high potential drilling rates, the economic potential of the spark, erosion, explosive, and forced-flame drills should be carefully evaluated. The jet-piercing drill is already widely used for drilling highly spallable rocks such as taconite.

Electric disintegration drills could produce high drilling rates in highly spallable rocks with high electrical conductivity, but only a few rocks fall into this category, so this drill has only limited potential application. Pellet and turbine drills can drill at rates nearly comparable to conventional drills, but they are limited by low power output and low efficiency. Electric arc and high-frequency electric drills can possibly drill hard, spallable rocks faster than rotary drills can, but they appear to have little advantage over jet-piercing drills with their much higher power outputs. Plasmas are high heat-transfer devices and should be considered for any application where it is necessary to rapidly heat rock or other materials. With the current state of the art, plasmas appear to have little advantage over jet-piercing drills, except possibly in small or wet holes or where the combustion products from the oxygen–fuel oil flame create a problem. Because of their low drilling rates, the remainder of the novel drills in Table 48 appear to have little potential application for large-scale rock drilling at this time. These low drilling rates result primarily from low power transmission to the rock and from the high specific energy required to fuse and vaporize rock. For example, a 10 kw laser transmitting 70 percent of its output power to the rock would fuse a 20 cm diameter hole at only 0.3–0.6 cm/min. Even this is optimistic, because the largest current commercial laser has a power output of only 1 kw. A laser output of 10–20 kw was used as the example in Table 48 because of the rapid advances being made in laser technology. For example, the power outputs of lasers has increased over fiftyfold during the last 3 years; their efficiency has increased by 1500 percent. As the power outputs of lasers and these other devices increase, their drilling rates and potential applications will increase. For this reason, it is important to continually reevaluate these devices as new equipment and better techniques are developed.

The power density and drilling rate for most of the drills in Table 48 are nearly independent of the diameter of the drill. A few of the drills such as laser, electron beam, and erosion can produce very high-power concentrations in applications where the drill can be placed outside of the hole. For example, electron beams and lasers can produce power concentrations of 10^9 and 10^{12} w/cm^2 respectively. Assuming that 50 percent of the output power is utilized, these power concentrations could fuse small-diameter holes in rock at rates of 10^5 and 10^8 cm/sec. A drilling rate of 100 cm/min could be produced by a 20 h.p. electron beam drill in a 0.75 cm diameter hole and by a 2 h.p. laser drill in a 0.24 cm diameter hole, assuming 50 percent of the output power is utilized [eq. (8)]. This is faster than conventional drills can drill most medium and hard rocks (Table 3, p. 12), which indicates that these devices have potential application for drilling small-diameter holes. Erosion drills can also produce high-power concentrations and high drilling rates in small holes. For example, a 690 h.p. erosion water jet has drilled a 1.31 cm diameter hole in sandstone at an instantaneous rate of 200 cm/sec (Table 18, p. 42).

Many factors must be considered when evaluating the economic potential of these new drilling methods. Oilfield drilling is currently done with very large expensive rigs requiring crews of four or more men. New drilling methods that would use smaller rigs, smaller crews, or flexible drill pipe to increase trip speed could be economical although they drilled slower than conventional drills. In oilfield drilling, the cost of the power transmitted to the rock by the bit is relatively insignificant compared to the other costs, so novel drills that require considerably more power could be economical if they drilled faster or if they reduced the capital or operating costs.

Consideration should be given to combining two or more of these novel drilling methods. For example, lasers could be used to cut slots in rocks and sparks or erosion jets could be used to crush and remove the unsupported rock. Novel drills could also be combined with conventional drills; e.g. lasers, plasmas, or electron beams could be used to heat and degrade rock and roller or drag bits could be used to remove the weakened rock.

This study has shown that some of these new drilling methods can drill large-diameter holes faster than conventional drills can in some rocks. A few of these drills produce very high-power concentrations and may have application for machining metals or brittle materials.

In conclusion, a considerable amount of research on new drilling techniques is going on throughout the world. Because of the rapid progress being made, some of these drills should find initial application in the next few years. Initially, these drills will probably be used for special applications such as stimulating oil wells or military

Power and Energy Requirements for Novel Drilling Methods

THE estimated maximum drilling rates for each of the drills in Table 48 are based on available data and the current state of the art. About 1500 joules/cm³ is required to heat rock to a spalling temperature of 400–600°C, and about 5000 joules/cm³ is required to fuse rock (Chapter 2).

Following is a brief description of how the specific energy and the power transmitted to the rock were estimated for each of the drills in Table 48. Equipment and techniques are continually improving, so these new drills should continually be re-evaluated as new equipment is developed and as new data become available. The reader can easily substitute new values of power output or specific energy and re-calculate the new potential drilling rate from eq. (8) or (30).

Electric Arc

A maximum of 200–300 electrical horsepower can be transmitted to the drill at the hole bottom (Drilling Research Inc.). Only about 15–30 percent of this power is transmitted to the rock by an electric arc drill (see Chapter 7), so a field size electric arc drill could transmit a maximum of about 45–90 h.p. to the rock.

Electric Disintegration Drill

A laboratory electric disintegration drill required 1000–2000 joules/cm³ to drill 2.5 cm diameter holes in concrete at rates up to 64 cm/min (Table 30). In these tests, up to 13.5 h.p. was transmitted to the concrete; this would extrapolate to 880 h.p. for a 20 cm dia-meter drill. For this larger drill, the power output delivered to the hole bottom would be limited to 200–300 h.p. Assuming that 50 percent of the heat is conducted away from the hole bottom, this would correspond to an effective power of 100–150 h.p. transmitted to the rock. In rocks with lower electrical conductivity (such as most sandstone and limestone), the power output would be limited by the amount of power which the rock would accept from the drill and could therefore be much less than 100 h.p.

Electric Heater Drill

The power output of an electric heater drill is limited by the rate at which heat can be conducted from the resistance heating element to the rock. A 5.1 cm diameter laboratory electric heater drill (Table 39) transmitted 6.7 h.p. to granite and basalt. This power density corresponds to 100 h.p. output for a 20 cm diameter drill.

In these laboratory tests, only about 40 percent of the power was utilized in fusing rock (Chapter 7), so the 20 cm diameter drill would transmit a maximum effective power output of about 40 h.p. to the rock. With additional development, this could probably be increased to about 50–100 h.p.

Erosion Drill

Erosion drills using 1–2 mm diameter nozzles (Tables 17, 19, and 20) require from 10,000 to 30,000 joules/cm³ to drill sandstone, limestone, marble, and granite, while drills using nozzles with 3–5 mm diameters require only 2000–4000 joules/cm³ to drill sandstone (Table 18). With sufficient pump capacity, an erosion drill could have a continuous power output of 1000–2000 h.p. A 1000 h.p. output could be produced pumping 100 l. of water per minute at a pressure of 5000 atm. Nozzles with power outputs in excess of 1650 h.p. have already been tested for short drilling times (Table 18).

Explosive Drill

In field tests (Table 13), Soviet explosive drills required from 200 to 400 joules/cm³ to drill sedimentary rocks. These explosive drills have a maximum power output of 68 h.p., i.e. 12 explosive capsules (50 g) per minute. Faster pumping rates produced sympathetic detonation of capsules in the drill pipe, while larger capsules increased the hole diameter but not the drilling rate. Additional development could possibly increase the power output of this drill to 100 h.p.

Forced-flame Drill

The Soviets have tested forced-flame drills which burn nitric acid and fuel oil. These drills have power outputs about three times greater than jet-piercing drills and can transmit from 300 to 600 h.p. to the rock (Chapter 6).

High-frequency Electric Drill

The high-frequency electric drill is designed to drill rocks with relatively high electrical conductivity (such as iron quartzite) by dielectric and resistance heating. Laboratory data (Kravchenko *et al.*, Young) indicate that a 20 cm diameter drill could transmit a maximum of about 30–60 h.p. to most rocks. With highly conductive rocks such as magnetite, the power output transmitted to the hole bottom would be limited to 200–300 h.p., but high-frequency electricity would not be required since in highly conductive rock resistance heating (which is independent of frequency) predominates.

Induction Drill

Laboratory data (Table 48) indicate that a 20 cm diameter induction drill could transmit a maximum of only 5–10 h.p. to a rock (such as magnetite) with high magnetic susceptibility. Because of their lower magnetic susceptibility, power output would be considerably less in most other rocks.

Jet-piercing Drill

Jet-piercing drills can drill highly spallable rocks such as taconite at rates of 10–20 cm/min. A specific-energy of about 1500 joules/cm^3 is required to spall rock, which indicates that about 107–214 effective horsepower is transmitted to the rock and utilized in spalling. These drills have power outputs of 500–1000 h.p., which indicates that considerable power is lost in various ways (such as heat or kinetic energy in the hot gases leaving the hole bottom, heat contained in vaporized water, or heat conducted away from the hole bottom).

Laser Drill

The gas laser described in Table 47 is one of the largest current lasers. It is 15 percent efficient and has a power output of 1 kw. The power output of lasers has increased over fiftyfold during the last 3 years, and continued improvement in power output and efficiency can be expected. For this reason, a 10–20 kw laser (13.6–27.2 h.p.) is used to estimate drilling rate in Table 48. The amount of energy reflected from the rock surface increases with increased power densities, so transmission efficiencies of 90, 70, and 50 percent will be assumed for spalling, fusion, and vaporization, respectively. Additional laboratory data on the transmission efficiency of laser beams to rocks are needed to evaluate the potential of laser drills more accurately.

Microwave Drill

Because of the space limitation, the largest magnetron that could be placed at the bottom of a 20 cm diameter hole would have a power output on the order of 10–20 h.p. For mining or tunneling applications slightly larger power outputs are possible since the magnetrons can be placed outside of the hole.

Nuclear Drill

The diameter of a nuclear drill would probably be limited to a minimum of 50–100 cm due to the size of the nuclear reactor. Its drilling rate would be limited by the rate at which heat can be conducted to the rock. The power density would be about equal to that of the electric heater drill since similar heat-conducting shells could be used in both drills. This power density corresponds to a power output of 1250–2500 h.p. for a 100 cm diameter nuclear drill. Since the power densities are equal, the maximum potential drilling rates for these two drills are also equal.

Pellet Drill

A 23 cm diameter pellet drill required 130 and 2500 joules/cm³ to drill limestone and quartzite, respectively (Table 8). These data indicate that about 200–400 joules/cm³ is required to drill medium-strength rocks. This drill had a power output of 6.4 h.p., which could possibly be increased to 10–20 h.p. by additional development.

Plasma Drill

Plasmas are about 60–80 percent efficient, and about 30–50 percent of the output power is transmitted to the rock. The maximum overall efficiency for a plasma drill is therefore on the order of 40 percent. A maximum of 200–300 electrical horsepower can be delivered to a plasma drill at the hole bottom, so a maximum of 80–120 h.p. can be transmitted to the rock.

Spark Drill

A laboratory spark drill required 95 joules/cm³ to drill shale, 235 joules/cm³ to drill quartz, and 340 joules/cm³ to drill marble (based on power output of the spark drill). These tests indicate that 200–400 joules/cm³ is required to drill medium-strength rocks. The power output of a spark drill is limited by the size of high-voltage capacitor that can be placed at the hole bottom. For a 20 cm diameter hole the capacitor would be limited to about 5–10 μf; this would limit the power output to about 100–200 h.p. A 200 h.p. output would be produced by discharging an 8.4 μf capacitor charged to 60 kv at the rate of 10 sparks/sec.

Turbine Drill

A field turbine drill (Table 5) drilled sedimentary rocks at rates of 1–5 m/hr. The power output of the drill was on the order of 20 h.p., which corresponds to a specific energy of 360–1300 joules/cm³. Additional development could possibly increase the power output of this drill to 30–40 h.p.

Ultrasonic Drill

Laboratory data (Tables 21–24) show that ultrasonic devices require from 10,000 to 120,000 joules/cm³ to drill various rocks. Medium-strength rocks appear to require about 20,000–30,000 joules/cm³. One of the largest current ultrasonic machinery devices (Neppiras, 1964) has a power input rating of 4 kw and a power output of about 2 kw. Although this drill could not be placed in a 20 cm diameter hole, its power output of 2 kw is used in Table 48, since even this favorable value predicts a very small drilling rate in a 20 cm diameter hole.

APPENDIX 2

Conversion Table

Atmosphere metric	× 1.0	= Kilogram/square centimeter
Centigrade degree	× 1.8 + 32	= Fahrenheit degree
Centimeter	× .394	= Inch
Cubic centimeter	× .061	= Cubic inch
Gram	× .0353	= Ounce avoirdupois
Gram	× .0022	= Pound avoirdupois
Gram/cubic centimeter	× 62.4	= Pound/cubic foot
Gram-calorie	× .00397	= BTU
Gram-calorie	× 3.09	= Foot-pound
Horsepower metric	× 75	= Kilogram-meter/second
Horsepower metric	× .986	= Horsepower U.S.
Joule	× .239	= Gram-calorie
Joule	× 1.0	= Watt-second
Joule	× .738	= Foot-pound
Joule/cubic centimeter	× 12.1	= Foot-pound/cubic inch
Joule/cubic centimeter	× 145	= Pound/square inch
Kilogram	× 2.2	= Pound avoirdupois
Kilogram-meter	× 7.23	= Foot-pound
Kilogram/square centimeter	× 14.22	= Pound/square inch
Kilowatt	× 1.36	= Horsepower metric
Liter	× 61	= Cubic inch
Liter	× .0353	= Cubic feet
Liter	× .264	= Gallon liquid U.S.
Meter	× 3.28	= Feet
Micron	× .0001	= Centimeter
Millimeter mercury	× 1.36	= Gram/square centimeter
Millimeter mercury	× .0193	= Pound/square inch
Oersted	× .796	= Ampere turn/centimete
Square centimeter	× .155	= Square inch

References

1. Abrasive drilling: potential new tool for mining, *Eng. Min. J.*, **166**, 108–9 (Sept. 1965).
2. ADAMS, C. M., JR. and HARDWAY, G. A., Fundamentals of laser beam machining and drilling, *IEEE Transactions, IGA* **1** (2) (March/April 1965).
3. ADAMS, W. M., Nuclear Reactor Apparatus for Earth Penetration, U.S. Patent No. 3155194 (1965).
4. AGOSHKIN, M. I. and VORNYUK, A. S., Secondary breaking of iron ores by high-frequency current, *Izv. Akad. Nauk USSR*, No. 1 (Jan. 1960), pp. 138–44. English transl. No. 4857 by Henry Brutcher Technical Translations, P.O. Box 157, Altadena, California.
5. ARMSTRONG, D. E., COLEMAN, J. S., MCINTEER, B. B., POTTER, R. M., and ROBINSON, E. A., *Rock Melting as a Drilling Technique*, Pub. No. LA3243D Clearinghouse, U.S. Dept. Commerce, Springfield, Virginia (March 1965).
6. AUSTIN, C. F., *Lined-cavity Shaped Charges and their Use in Rock and Earth Materials*, Bulletin 69, State Bureau of Mines and Mineral Resources, Campus Station, Socorro, New Mexico (1959).
7. BAKISH, R., *Introduction to Electron Beam Technology*, Wiley & Sons, N.Y. (1962).
8. BERGSTROM, B. H., The electrohydraulic crusher, *Eng. Min. J.*, **162**, 134 (Feb. 1961).
9. BOND, F. C., *Crushing and Grinding Calculations*, Bulletin No. 07R9235B, Allis-Chalmers Manufacturing Company, Milwaukee, Wisconsin (Jan. 1961).
10. BOUCHE, R. E., Drilling rocks with plasma jets, MS thesis T-992, Colorado School of Mines (1964).
11. BRICHKIN, A. V. and BOLOTOV, A. V., Use of an electric arc for rock boring, *Izvestiia Vysshikh Uchebnykh Zavedenii: Tsvetsnaia Metallurgia USSR*, **5**, 7–14 (May 1966).
12. BROWNING, J. A., Method and apparatus for impacting a stream at high velocity against a surface to be treated, U.S. Patent No. 2990653 (1961).
13. BROWNING, J. A., HORTON, W. R., and HARTMAN, H. L., Recent advances in flame jet working of minerals, *Proceedings 7th Symposium on Rock Mechanics, Penn. State University*, pp. 281–313 (June 14–16, 1965).
14. BUNSHAH, R. F., High-power electron beams, *Int. Sci. Tech.*, pp. 30–38 (April 1962).
15. BURLUTSKII, B. D., VEDYAEV, Y. M., and PETRENKO, N. P., The thermal destruction of rock by means of an electric arc, *Gornyi Zhurnal*, No. 12 (1959).
16. CALAMAN, J. J. and ROLSETH, H. C., Technical advances expand use of jet-piercing process in taconite industry, *Mining Research*, Pergamon Press, p. 473 (1962).
17. CANNON, G. E., Development of a high-speed low-torque drilling device, presented at fall AIME meeting, Dallas, Texas (Oct. 6–9, 1957).
18. CARSLAW, H. S. and JAEGER, J. C., *Conduction of Heat in Solids*, 2nd edition, Clarendon Press, Oxford (1959).

19. CARLEY-MACAULY, K. W., HITCHON, J. W., and MAROUDAS, N. G., *Energy Consumption in Electrohydraulic Crushing*, British Atomic Energy Research Establishment Report R5054 (1965).
20. Drilling Research Inc., Annual Reports, Houston, Texas, 1949–53.
21. Drilling test is proposed for novel pellet boring system, *Drilling*, p. 148 (July 1958).
22. Drilling with radar, *Min. Eng. J.*, p. 24 (April 1963).
23. ECKEL, J. E., DEILY, F. H., and LEDGERWOOD, L. W., Development and testing of jet pump pellet impact drill bits, *Trans. AIME* **207**, 1–9 (1956).
24. ECKEL, J. E., Esso Production Research Company, Houston, Texas, Personal Communications, 1967.
25. Electronic rock breaking, *S. African Min. Eng. J.*, **73**, 335–6 (August 17 1962).
26. EPPERSON, J. P., DYER, W., and GRZYWA, J. C., The laser now a production tool, *Western Electric Engineer* (April 1966).
27. EPSHTEYN, E. F., ARSH, E. I., and VITORT, G. K., New methods of crushing rock, *Gosud. Naushno-Tekh. Izad. Neft. i Gorno-Topliv Noi Literatery Moscow*, 1960. Translation No. 62-11712, U.S. Dept. of Commerce, Office of Technical Services, Washington 25, D.C.
28. FARMER, I. W., Rock fracture by water jet impact, *Colliery Engineer* (February 1967).
29. FARMER, I. W. and ATTEWELL, P. B., Rock penetration by high velocity water jet, *Int. J. Rock Mech. Min. Sci.* **2**, No. 2 (July 1965).
30. FINNIE, I., and OH, H., An analysis of rock drilling by erosion, *Proc. 1st Int. Cong. on Rock Mech., Lisbon, Portugal* (Sept. 25–Oct. 1, 1966).
31. FREEMAN, D. C., SAWDYE, J. A. and MUMPTON, F. A., The mechanism of thermal spalling in rocks, *Eleventh Symposium on Exploratory Drilling, Colorado School of Mines, Quarterly*, **58**, No. 4 (1963).
32. FRIEDLANDER, D., Gruman conducting study of ruby laser capabilities, *Metalworking News*, p. 4 (Feb. 3, 1964).
33. GELLER, L. B., Research in improved methods of rock breakage, *Trans. Inst. Min. Metal.* (July 1967).
34. GIANNINI, G. M., The plasma jet, *Sci. Am.* **197**, 80–88 (Feb. 1957).
35. GINTSBURG, M. A., Disintegration of rocks by H.F. electromagnetic fields, *Izv. Akad. Nauk USSR*, No. 10 (Oct. 1957), Trans. by Henry Brutcher Tech. Transl., P.O. Box 157, Altadena, California.
36. GLADSTONE, R. A., and KETTANEH, A., *News Release Regarding Use of Lasers to Thermally Degrade Rock*, Office of Public Relations, Massachusetts Institute of Tech., Cambridge, Mass., November 24, 1966.
37. GOLDMAN, R., *Ultrasonic Technology*, Reinhold Publishing Corporation, London, England (1962).
38. GORDON, J. P., The maser, *Sci. Am.* **149**, No. 6 (Dec. 1963).
39. GRAY, W. M., Surface spalling by thermal stresses in rock, *Proc. Rock Mechanics Symposium, Mines Branch Department of Mines and Technical Surveys, Ottawa*, pp. 85–106 (1965).
40. GRONER, W., Lasers, *Electronics World*, p. 31 (Aug. 1965).
41. HEINS, R. W., and FRIZ, T. O., The effect of low temperature on some physical rock properties, *Proceedings 3rd Conference on Drilling and Rock Mechanics, University of Texas, Austin, Texas* (Jan. 1967).
42. High-power efficiency offered by CO_2 laser, *Sci. Res.* **1** (12), 47 (Dec. 1966).
43. Hot drill penetrates ice, *Petr. Week.* (April 7, 1961), pp. 26–27.
44. HOWE, R. J., Esso Production Research Company, Houston, Texas, Personal Communications, 1963.

45. IRONMAN, R., Microwave drilling uses radar, *Rock Products*, p. 119 (Feb. 1963).
46. *Jet-piercing Research Project*, Mines Branch Investigation Report IR62-27, Department of Mines and Technical Surveys, Ottawa, Canada (1962).
47. JUST, G. D., The jet-piercing process, *Quarry Managers' J., Inst. of Quarrying Trans.*, pp. 219–26 (June 1963).
48. KELLEY, J., Electron beam machining, *British Communications and Electronics*, pp. 20–23 (Jan. 1964).
49. KELLNER, J. M., and ROBERTS, A. P., Hydraulic wall-anchored drill collar promises low drilling costs, *Oil and Gas. J.*, p. 87 (Oct. 3, 1960).
50. KORMAN, S., High-intensity arcs, *Int. Sci. Tech.*, pp. 90–98 (June 1964).
51. KRAVCHENKO, V. S., The search for new methods of breaking down hard rock, *Gornyi Zhurnal USSR*, No. 1, 36–43 (1957).
52. KRAVCHENKO, V. S., OBVASTOV, A. P., and USTINOV, V. V., Dustless breaking of rocks electrically, translated in *Min. Congr. J.*, pp. 53–55 (May 1961).
53. KULLE, P. A., and PONOMAREV, P. V., Nature of the electrohydraulic method and possibilities of using it in drilling wells, *Vees. Nauchno-Issle Skii Inst. Method i Tekh. Razv. Trudy USSR*, No. 1 (1958).
54. LATOUR, H. and WREN, H. D., Mining of Taconite Ores Using High Frequency Magnetic Energy, U.S. Patent No. 2859952 (1958).
55. LEACH, S. J., and WALKER, G. L., The application of high-speed liquid jets to cutting, *Phil. Trans.* A, **260**, 295–308 (1966).
56. LEDGERWOOD, L. W., JR., Efforts to develop improved oil-well drilling methods, *J. Pet. Tech.*, pp. 61–74 (April 1960).
57. MACK, R. C., Laser, *Western Aerospace*, pp. 16–33 (Oct. 1962).
58. MAROUDAS, N. G., *Electrohydraulic Crushing*, British Atomic Energy Research Establishment Report No. R4550 (1964).
59. MAROUDAS, N. E., JOHNSON, H. A., and YIGIT, E., The mechanism of electrohydraulic crushing, Dechema–Monographien No. 993–1026, Vol. 57, Zerkleinern, p. 551 (1967).
60. MAROUDAS, N. G., and TAYLOR, R. F., *Interim Report on the Electrohydraulic Crushing of Refractory Materials*, Atomic Energy Research Establishment Report No. M1261 (1964).
61. MAROVELLI, R. L., Bureau of Mines Research Center, Minneapolis, Minnesota, personal communications (1967).
62. MAROVELLI, R. L., CHEN, T. S., and VEITH, K. F., Thermal fragmentation of rock, *Trans. Soc. Min. Eng.* (Mar. 1966).
63. MARTIN, E. A., The underwater spark an example of gaseous conduction at about 100,000 atmospheres, *J. Appl. Phys.* **31** (2), 255 (1960).
64. MAURER, W. C., The "perfect-cleaning" theory of rotary drilling, *J. Pet. Tech.*, **14** (11), 1270 (Nov. 1962).
65. MAURER, W. C., Bit-tooth penetration under simulated borehole conditions, *J. Pet. Tech.* (Dec. 1965).
66. MAURER, W. C., The state of rock mechanics knowledge in drilling, Chapter 15 of *Failure and Breakage of Rock*, Port City Press, Inc., Baltimore, Maryland, p. 355 (1967).
67. MAURER, W. C. and RINEHART, J. S., Impact crater formation in rock, *J. Appl. Phys.*, **31** (7), 1247 (July 1960).
68. Methods of an apparatus for splitting non-metallic brittle materials, English Patent No. 1019737 (1966).
69. McGEE, E., New down-hole tool, *Oil and Gas J.*, **54** (Aug. 8, 1955).

70. Microwaves split granite, concrete, *Electronics*, **36** (48), 38 (Nov. 29, 1963).
71. New drill concepts, *Eng. Min. J.*, pp. 239–58 (June 1966).
72. New drill subjects rock to "hot and cold" shock, *Eng. Min. J.*, p. 103 (March 1965).
73. New role for R-F energy: rock busting, *Electronics*, p. 11 (Sept. 22, 1961).
74. New thermal drill bit melts its way in rock, *Eng. Min. J.* **166**, 104–5 (May 1965).
75. NEPPIRAS, E. A., Ultrasonic machining, *Modern Workshop Technology*, Part 2, Cleaver-Hume Press (1959).
76. NEPPIRAS, E. A., Ultrasonic machining and forming, *Ultrasonic*, **2**, 167–73 (Dec. 1964).
77. NEPPIRAS, E. A., Imperial College of Science and Technology, London, England, personal communications, 1967.
78. OSTROVSKII, N. P., Deep-hole drilling with explosives, *Gostoptekhia 'dat Moscow*, 1960, trans. by Consultants Bureau Enterprises, Inc., New York.
79. Penn. State meeting gives "last word" on drilling-blasting tools and methods, *Eng. Min. J.*, pp. 97–98 (Aug. 1965).
80. RAYNAL, J., Discussion of paper "Efforts to develop improved oilwell drilling methods" by L. W. Ledgerwood, *J. Pet. Tech.* **219**, 63–67 (Dec. 1960).
81. Reactor to burn through earth's crust?, *New Scientist*, p. 518 (March 1962).
82. REED, T. B., Plasma torches, *Int. Sci. Tech.* (June 1962).
83. ROBINSON, L. H., Drilling by explosives, *Proceedings 7th Symposium on Rock Mechanics, Penn. State University*, pp. 462–89 (June 14–16, 1965).
84. ROBINSON, L. H., Experimental tests of a method for drilling with explosives, *Soc. Petr. Eng. J.*, **5** (2), 153–9 (June, 1965).
85. ROSS, S. L., Excavating apparatus and method, U.S. Patent No. 3152651 (1964).
86. RUBOW, I. H., Jet-piercing in taconite, *Mines Magazine*, Colo. School of Mines (March 1956).
87. Sand-slurry perforating is perfected, *Petroleum Week*, p. 24 (July 3, 1959).
88. SARAPUU, E., Electrical disintegration drilling, *Rock Mechanics*, Pergamon Press, pp. 173–84 (1963).
89. SARAPUU, E., Electrical fracturing and crushing of taconite, *Proceedings 7th Symposium on Rock Mechanics, Penn. State University, University Park, Pennsylvania*, pp. 314–24 (July 14–16, 1965).
90. SCHÜLER, O., Zerkleinerung mit Hilfe Electromagnetischer Schwingung, *Aachener Blätter*, **11**, 165–90 (1961).
91. SHAPIR, YA. I., Research in forced-flame drilling in the Altyn-Topkan and Krivorozh Quarries, *Proc. of the All-Union Research Inst. for Drilling Tech. USSR*, No. 10, Moscow (1963).
92. *Smithsonian Physical Tables*, Smithsonian Institute, Washington, D.C. (1954).
93. SOLES, J. A., and GELLER, L. B., *Experimental Studies Relating to Minerological and Petrographic Features to the Thermal Piercing of Rocks*, Can. Dept. Mines and Tech. Survey, Ottawa, Rep. TB53 (Jan. 1964).
94. SOLEYEV, V. A., and REKSIN, S. E., USSR Authors Certificate No. 40914, 1935 (Electric Arc Drill).
95. Split second tubing cutter, *Oil Forum*, pp. 332–3 (Sept. 1955).
96. STEUDEL, J., Versuche mit Mikrowellen zur Zerstörung von Sandsteinen, *Gluckauf-Forschungshefte*, pp. 117–25 (April 1965).
97. SVIRIDOV, A. P., Semiautomatic Ultrasonic device *Izvestiya Vysshikh Uchebnykh Zavedenii: Priborostroenie USSR*, No. 2 (1958), 159–63.

98. TEALE, R., The concept of specific energy in rock drilling, *Int. J. Rock Mech. Min. Sci.* **2** (1), 57 (March 1965).
99. Thermal drill taps poles, *Machine Design*, p. 36 (March 16, 1961).
100. THORPE, M. L., Plasma jet-research tool, high temperature heat source, *Presented at 7th Int. Symposium on Combustion, Oxford University* (Aug. 28–Sept. 3, 1958).
101. THORPE, M. L., The plasma jet and its uses, *Research and Development*, **11** (1), 5–15 (Jan. 1960).
102. TITKOV, N. I., VARZANOV, M. A., SLEZINGER, I. I., PETROVA, O. P., and BORISOV, G. I., Drilling with electrical discharges in liquids, *Neft. Khoz. USSR*, **35** (10), 5–10 (1957). English translation by Associated Technical Services Inc., P.O. Box 271, East Orange, New Jersey.
103. *Turbine Bit*, Christensen Diamond Products Co., brochure.
104. UYEDA, S. and YABU, T., Some experiments on thermal shock fracture of rocks, *Bulletin of the Earthquake Research Institute*, **39**, 593 (1961).
105. VERTE, L. A., USSR Authors Certificate No. 75136, 1948 (Electric Arc Drill).
106. VOYTSEKHOVSKIY, B. V., NIKOLAEV, V. P., LUDIN, V. M., MAIER, O. F., and CHERMENSKII, G. P., Some results of the destruction of rocks by means of a pulsed water jet, *Izvestiya Sibirskogo Otdeleniya Akademii Nauk USSR*, English translation No. OTS: 64-21809, from U.S. Dept. of Commerce Office of Technical Services, Washington, D.C.
107. VOZDVIZHENSKII, B. I. and SKORNYAKOV, A. L., *Shot-hole drilling*, Gosudarstvennoe Nauchno-Tekhnicheskoe Izdatelistvo Literatury Gornomu Delu, Moscow (1960).
108. WILLIAMSON, T. N., and PARISH, V. W., *Excavation—Scientific and Technical Application Forecast*, Office of the Chief of Research and Development, Dept. of Army, Washington, D.C. (1964).
109. WÖHLBIER, H. and MATTHAEI, H., Die Electromagnetic-Thermische Gestein Zerstörung, *Proc. 1st Int. Cong. on Rock Mech., Lisbon, Portugal*, Sept. 25–Oct. 1, 1966.
110. YOUNG, F. M., The secondary breaking effect of heat-frequency electric energy applied to rock fragments, *Rock Mechanics*, Pergamon Press, Oxford, pp. 185–203 (1963).
111. YUTKIN, L. A., *Electrohydraulic Effect*, Mashgiz (State Scientific Technical Press for Machine Construction Literature), Moscow, 1955. Translation No. AD-267-722, Armed Services Technical Information Agency, Arlington Hall Station, Arlington 12, Virginia.

Index